STEMscopes™

CA-NGSS 3D

Student Notebook – Fifth Grade
ISBN: 978-1-63037-598-0

Published by Accelerate Learning, Inc., 5177 Richmond Ave, Suite 1025, Houston, TX 77056. Copyright © 2018, by Accelerate Learning, Inc. All rights reserved. No part of this publication may be reproduced or distributed in any form or by any means, or stored in a database or retrieval system, without prior written consent of Accelerate Learning, Inc., including, but not limited to, in any network or other electronic storage or transmission, or broadcast for distance learning.

To learn more, visit us at www.stemscopes.com.

10 9 8 7 6 5 4 3 2

This Student Notebook is designed to be used as a companion piece to our online curriculum.

The pages of this book are organized and follow the 5E model.

ENGAGE	**Student Handout**
	A short activity to grab students' interest

EXPLORE	**Explore**
	Hands-on tasks, including scientific investigations and engineering solutions
	Claim-Evidence-Reasoning (CER)
	A formative assessment in which students write a scientific explanation to show their understanding

EXPLAIN	**Linking Literacy**
	Strategies to help students comprehend difficult informational text

ELABORATE	**Reading Science**
	A reading passage about the concept that includes comprehension questions

EVALUATE	**Claim-Evidence-Reasoning (CER)**
	A summative assessment in which students write a scientific explanation to show their understanding
	Open-Ended Response (OER)
	A short-answer and essay assessment to evaluate mastery of the concept

Only student pages are included in this book, and directions on how to use these pages are found in our online curriculum. Use the URL address and password provided to you by your district to access our full curriculum.

Student Notebook - Fifth Grade
Table of Contents

Lesson

Page

California Instructional Segment
Mission Log

Mission Log

Anchoring Phenomena

How can we use the properties of matter to clean up water after a natural disaster?

Mission Briefing

A tsunami has hit the coast of California. You are on the disaster relief team. The team is in charge of developing a plan of action to reopen the drinking-water plant that provides clean drinking water to many cities. The plant has no electricity, contaminants in the water supply, and damage to concrete around the water tanks.

- What properties are helpful to consider when separating different kinds of matter?
- What tools can be used to help you separate mixtures?
- What materials are good electrical insulators?

California Instructional Segment
Mission Log

Class Mission Log

Information Gained

Matter Is Everywhere

What evidence tells you that matter is made up of particles too small to be seen?

Changes to Matter

How does a change in state affect the weight of matter?

Connection to Mission

Matter Is Everywhere

Write a procedure including tools and steps you will take for separating a dissolved substance from the water.

Changes to Matter

There is a cooler of water bottles and ice for the team. What will happen to the weight of the cooler and its contents after the ice melts?

California Instructional Segment
Mission Log

Class Mission Log

Information Gained

Properties of Matter

What are the properties of matter that can be used to identify different types of materials?

List as many insulators and conductors of electricity as you can in the T-chart below.

Insulators	Conductors

Connection to Mission

Properties of Matter

Write a procedure including the tools and steps you will take for separating the wood pellets and steel cans from the water.

Electrical wires are exposed. Describe what materials you could use to cover the exposed parts to keep everyone safe.

California Instructional Segment
Mission Log

Class Mission Log

Information Gained	Connection to Mission
Mixtures	**Mixtures**
What happens to the properties of sand and water when they are mixed together?	You will need to patch the concrete. You fill a bucket with 10 lb of concrete and 5 gallons of water. A gallon of water weighs about 8 lb. How much does the mixture weigh once it is combined in the bucket?
List the different signs that would tell you a chemical change happened.	As you mix the concrete with water, you notice the bucket getting warmer. What does this tell you?

Name: _____

Date: _____

California Instructional Segment

Action Plan

Action Plan

Develop a plan of action to clean up the water, restore the power, and repair the concrete at the drinking-water plant.

Here's what we know:

- Large bags of salt were used to try to block dirty water from entering the drinking-water tank, but the bags are now empty. We can assume salt has gotten into the tank.

- Steel cans of cleaning products have sunk to the bottom of the water tank.

- Small wood pellets were found floating at the top of the tank.

- The power lines have been damaged, and some wires are exposed.

- Patches of concrete around the tank have been chipped and need to be repaired with new concrete.

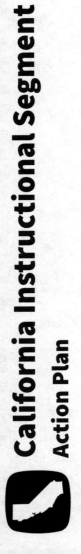

California Instructional Segment

Action Plan

Take Action

Write a detailed plan describing how you will clean up the water, restore the power, and repair the concrete at the drinking-water plant.

Matter Is Everywhere

Graphic Organizer

Where is the Matter?!

Directions: In each box, draw and label a picture of a time when you knew matter was there but could not see it. Use the lines below your picture to explain how you knew the matter was there.

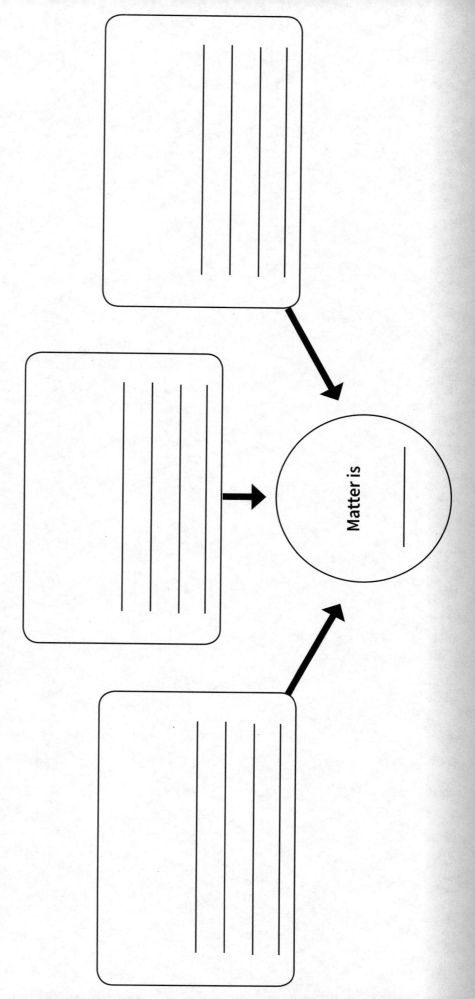

Matter is _____

Name: _____ Date: _____

Explore 2

Contaminated Water

The Problem

Pablo likes growing plants in the school garden. He uses three different water sources every day to water different sections of the garden. He noticed that some of the plants started wilting, so he is concerned one water supply has been contaminated. He decided to send the water samples to different labs (student groups) to find out if there is any contamination in the samples.

The Challenge

Each lab (group) will be given three samples of water that has been used to water the plants. Find which sample has been contaminated and report it back to Pablo. You will also need to teach Pablo how to test his own water in the future.

Criteria and Constraints

- You may **not** taste the samples.
- You will have 10 minutes to come up with a solution and then test your samples.
- You will need to make a list of materials needed and give it to your teacher for approval.
- You must follow all lab safety rules put in place by your teacher.

Brainstorm and Research

Write down any ideas you have about how you could master the challenge. If you need more information, write down what you need to know and gain permission from your teacher to research the answer.

Explore 2

Design Plan

Use the ideas you wrote down while brainstorming to develop a final design plan. Draw your plan and label the materials. Be sure to list what each material will be used for.

Build and Test

Follow your plan to test it. Does it meet all the criteria and constraints? Use the space below to list what problems you need to fix in your design.

_____

_____

_____

Refine and Redesign

How could you solve the problems you found during testing? Use the space below to create a new plan that should solve the problems.

 **Explore 2**

Retest and Finalize

Complete your new test. Does it meet all the criteria and constraints? If not, repeat the refine and redesign process. If it does, move on to planning your presentation.

Presentation Plan

Use the space below to plan how you will present your testing process and findings to Pablo. Be sure to include who will speak and what you want to say. Your presentation should include the scientific ideas used to solve this design challenge.

Linking Literacy
During-Reading

Anticipation Guide

Carefully read the statements below. Think about the statement and determine if you generally agree or disagree with it by marking an *X* next to your answer. As you read the article, select text that provides evidence for or against the statements. If you changed your mind based on the evidence from the text, mark if you now agree or disagree in a separate color.

Agree	Disagree	Statement:
		Matter is made of particles that cannot be seen, but we know they are there.
Paragraph Number		Evidence:

Agree	Disagree	Statement:
		Physical properties can be observed and measured. Some physical properties of matter—such as size, color, and shape—can be observed using your senses.
Paragraph Number		Evidence:

Linking Literacy
During-Reading

Agree	Disagree	Statement:
		Each state of matter has certain characteristics based on how its particles move.
Paragraph Number		**Evidence:**

Agree	Disagree	Statement:
		Sugar and sand both dissolve in water; they are classified as water-soluble.
Paragraph Number		**Evidence:**

Linking Literacy
Post-Reading

Matter Is . . . A–Z

Directions: Using an A–Z pattern, write an example of matter for each letter and a description of a few of its physical properties in the next column.

Matter	Description
A = Air	Add air to a basketball or soccer ball and it will expand.
B	
C	
D	
E	
F	
G	
H	
I	
J	
K	
L	
M	
N	

O	
P	
Q	
R	
S	
T	
U	
V	
W	
X	
Y	
Z	

Reading Science

The Great Ice Challenge

1. The fifth-grade class at Eagle Lake Elementary was learning about the states of matter. They learned that matter was anything that contained mass and had volume, such as a chair, a person, and even air. Their teacher, Ms. Jones, also told them that matter could change **states**, or forms, depending on the temperature.

2. "That does not make any sense," said Ivan. "A chair is always a chair, air is always air, and I'm always Ivan. I have never seen any of these change states."

3. "Hmm . . ." said Ms. Jones. "What if I can prove you wrong?"

4. The kids were excited, because this sounded like a challenge.

5. The kids gleefully accepted the challenge and anxiously watched as Ms. Jones showed them an ice cube on a tray.

6. "Is this ice cube matter?" she asked them as she held up one of the ice cubes.

7. "Sure," said Tamara. "It definitely has mass, because we can put it on the triple beam balance and weigh it, and it also has volume, because it takes up space. That ice cube is in a solid state of matter."

8. "Great. So we all agree that this is matter," Ms. Jones said. "I removed it from the cafeteria freezer just a moment ago, so let us observe what happens as it warms up."

9. The fifth graders got out their observation notebooks and watched closely. They took detailed notes as the ice cube began to drip, creating a small puddle in the middle of the tray. Tamara predicted that the ice cube might melt even faster if they raised the temperature.

10. "That's an interesting idea, Tamara," Ms. Jones said. "Can you think of a way that we might test your hypothesis?"

11. "I know!" said Tamara. "The overhead projector always heats up when we are using it. Let us place the tray on the projector and observe what happens then."

12. Ms. Jones transported the tray to the overhead projector. The increase in temperature did make the ice cube melt faster, just as Tamara had predicted. In the short amount of time since the ice had been removed from the freezer, the ice cube melted completely, and all that remained was a puddle of water.

13. "Okay," said Ivan. "I understand what you're saying. Melting is one way that matter can change states."

14. "Yes," said Ms. Jones. "Even the chair can change states. It is made of metal and plastic. If I heated it to a high-enough temperature, the metal and plastic would melt and become liquid, just like the ice."

15. "Yeah," said Bobby. "One time when my mom was cooking, she accidentally melted a plastic spoon on the stove top. It turned to liquid, and it smelled terrible!"

16. "Right. Matter changes states."

17. "You said even air can change," said Ivan. "You still have not given us evidence to prove your point."

18. "Just wait until tomorrow," said Ms. Jones.

19. The kids packed up to go home, and Ms. Jones left the tray of water out on the table overnight. The next morning, when the students returned to school, they observed the tray that had contained the puddle of water. The tray was dry!

20. "What happened?" asked Tamara.

21. "I bet I know!" said Ivan. "Heat caused the water to evaporate, and the liquid became a gas."

22. "Right. So where is the water now?" asked Ms. Jones.

23. "It is . . ." Ivan realized he had been beaten. "The water is in the air. So, now the air contains more water vapor than it did yesterday—and we lose the bet."

24. "Yes," said Ms. Jones. "The ice cube was in a solid state; then, due to heat, it melted into a puddle of water, which is a liquid state. Then, overnight, the temperature in the room caused the liquid to evaporate and become water vapor, which is a gas.

25. "However, the most important thing is that you were thinking like scientists, so I am going to give you that extra recess, anyway."

26. All the kids cheered.

Reading Science

1. Here are some dictionary definitions of the word **state**:

   1. (n) A nervous feeling

   2. (n) A territory of the government

   3. (n) The form of matter

   4. (n) A part of the United States of America

   Which definition is closest to the way the word **states** is used in the following sentence from the first paragraph?

   Their teacher, Ms. Jones, also told them that matter could change states, or forms, depending on the temperature.

   A. Definition 1

   B. Definition 2

   C. Definition 3

   D. Definition 4

2. Which term should be placed in the arrow?

   A. Evaporation

   B. Heat

   C. Gas

   D. Liquid

3. What was Tamara's hypothesis?

    A. The ice cube would evaporate.

    B. The ice cube would refreeze if they put it in the freezer.

    C. The ice cube would melt faster if they put it outside.

    D. The ice cube would melt faster if the temperature were raised.

4. Why did Ms. Jones give the students recess, even though they lost the bet?

    A. She was proud of their thinking.

    B. She wanted to take a break on Friday.

    C. She always let them have extra recess on Friday.

    D. They had behaved well.

5. In this story, what did Ivan learn?

    A. Always bet against Ms. Jones.

    B. Ms. Jones never keeps her promises.

    C. Matter can change states, even though a person may not be able to see it happen.

    D. Matter never changes.

Open-Ended Response

1. Matter is everywhere. What evidence do we have to prove this?

_____

_____

_____

_____

2. To prepare for a birthday party, you blow up balloons. Describe what happens to the balloon when you blow air into it. How does a balloon change its shape? Explain the processes happening inside of the balloon.

_____

_____

_____

_____

3. Lemonade was served at your friend's birthday party. You could tell that the lemonade had a great amount of sugar in it because of its sweet taste! Explain why you cannot see the sugar in the lemonade. How else could you prove it is there?

_____

_____

_____

_____

Claim-Evidence-Reasoning

Matter Is Everywhere

Scenario

Lea finished her lunch. All that is left is her plastic sandwich bag. Lea thinks there is no longer anything in the bag, but Paul disagrees. He thinks the bag is filled with air, and air is something.

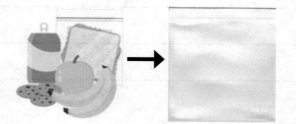

They decide to do an experiment to test each of their ideas, using two identical plastic baggies. They will measure and compare the mass and volume of an empty, flat, and sealed plastic bag with one that has been inflated with air and is "puffed up" and sealed. This will help them see if Lea's lunch bag is empty like she thinks or if Paul is correct and the bag is filled with air.

	Empty and Closed Bag	**Inflated and Closed Bag**
Mass (g)	6	7
Volume (cm³)	68	4,365

Prompt

Lea thinks that matter does not exist if it cannot be seen. Paul thinks matter can exist even when it is not visible. What do you think? Use the data in the chart to make a claim, provide your evidence, and explain your reasoning.

Claim-Evidence-Reasoning

Claim:

_____

_____

_____

_____

Evidence:

_____

_____

_____

_____

_____

_____

Reasoning:

_____

_____

_____

_____

_____

_____

_____

Changes to Matter

Name: _____   Date: _____

Graphic Organizer

Changes to Matter

Directions: Use this Graphic Organizer to take notes about the changes to matter and the weight of the matter you observed.

Freezing and Cooling

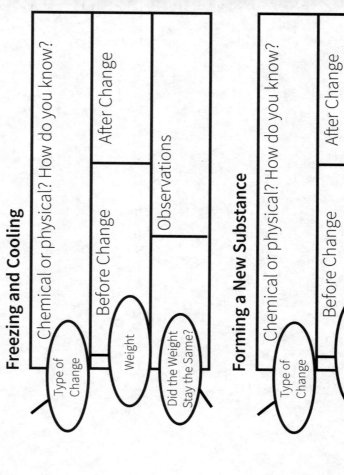

Type of Change

Chemical or physical? How do you know?

Before Change	After Change

Weight

Observations

Did the Weight Stay the Same?

Forming a New Substance

Type of Change

Chemical or physical? How do you know?

Before Change	After Change

Weight

Observations

Did the Weight Stay the Same?

Melting and Heating

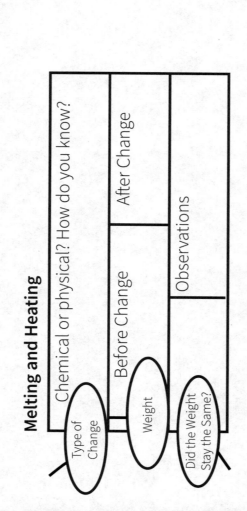

Type of Change

Chemical or physical? How do you know?

Before Change	After Change

Weight

Observations

Did the Weight Stay the Same?

Dissolving and Mixing

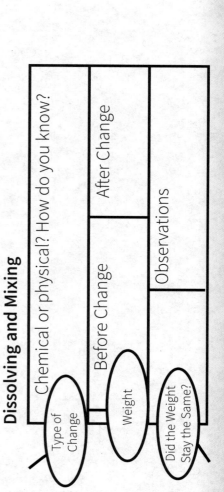

Type of Change

Chemical or physical? How do you know?

Before Change	After Change

Weight

Observations

Did the Weight Stay the Same?

Hook

Changing States

Material	Weight
Pie pan + plastic bag	
Pie pan + plastic bag + ice cube	
Ice cube only	
Pie pan + plastic bag + melted ice cube	
Melted ice cube only	

Use the space below to describe which physical properties of the ice cube changed and which stayed the same when it melted. Use data from the table to support your answer.

Explore 1

State of Matter Changes

Directions:

1. Select a material, place it on an aluminum pan, and measure the weight using a triple beam balance. Record this data in column *B* on the chart.
2. Place the pie pan with the material in it on a hot plate, and let the substance melt. Be sure to wear goggles when heating a material on a hot plate.
3. After the material has melted, use oven mitts (or the teacher's help) to move the pan from the hot plate back to the triple beam balance.
4. Measure the material's weight on the triple beam balance again. Record this data in column *C* on the chart.
5. Repeat the previous steps for each material (gummy candy, shortening, chocolate, and butter).
6. Be sure to turn off the hot plate as soon as your group is done heating all materials.
7. Answer questions 1–3 on the next page.
8. Place the pie pan with melted materials aside (off the hot plate) and allow time for the materials to become solid again.
9. Answer question 4 on the next page.
10. Once all the materials have cooled, place the aluminum pans on the triple beam balance to measure the weight.
11. Record the weight in column *D* of the data table below.
12. Answer questions 5–6 on the next page.
13. Graph your data in a triple-bar graph on the last page.

 **Explore 1**

A: Material	B: Weight of Material + Pie Pan before State Change	C: Weight of Melted Material + Pie Pan after State Change	D: Weight of Solid Material + Pie Pan after Second State Change
Shortening			
Gummy candy			
Chocolate			
Butter			

 **Explore 1**

1. What happened when we added heat to each substance?

_____

_____

_____

_____

2. How did the weight before melting the substance compare with the weight after melting the substance?

_____

_____

_____

_____

3. Why do you think the weight was the same after the substance melted?

_____

_____

_____

_____

 **Explore 1**

4. What do you think will happen to the weight once the materials return to their solid state?

_____

_____

_____

_____

5. Why did the material turn back into a solid?

_____

_____

_____

_____

6. Did the weight change after the material returned to a solid?

_____

_____

_____

_____

Explore 1

Create a triple-bar graph that represents the data collected in the chart. Be sure to add a label and scale to each axis and give your graph a title.

Title _____

Before melting	After melting	After cooling	Before melting	After melting	After cooling	Before melting	After melting	After cooling	Before melting	After melting	After cooling
Shortening			Gummy candy			Chocolate			Butter		

Explore 1

State of Matter Changes
Claim-Evidence-Reasoning

Prompt

Write a scientific explanation describing whether or not a change in the physical state of matter changes the matter's weight.

Claim:

_____

_____

_____

Evidence:

_____

_____

_____

Reasoning:

_____

_____

_____

_____

_____

Explore 2

Sweet Tea

Directions:

1. Fill the plastic cup with 100 mL of water.

2. Find the weight of the cup of water, using the triple beam balance, and record the data.

3. Find the weight of the instant tea drink mix and record the data. Remember to find the weight of only the instant tea drink mix by subtracting the weight of any container you use to measure it in.

4. Pour the drink mix into the water and stir until the mix has dissolved.

5. Answer question 1 on the next page.

6. Find the weight of the cup of tea again, using the triple beam balance, and record the data.

7. Answer question 2 on the next page.

8. Find the weight of the sugar and record the data. Remember to find the weight of the sugar only (the sugar without its container).

9. Add the sugar to the drink and stir until the sugar has dissolved.

10. Find the weight of the drink on the triple beam balance and record the data.

11. Answer questions 3–6 on the next page.

Material	Weight
Cup of water (cup + 100 mL water)	
Instant tea mix	
Cup of water + instant tea mix	
Sugar (2 tsp)	
Cup of water + instant tea mix + sugar	

1. How do you know the tea is in the water?

_____

_____

2. Did the weight of the solution change?

_____

_____

3. Why do you think we needed to find the weight of the single ingredient without including the weight of its container?

_____

_____

4. If you cannot see the sugar anymore in the drink, why did the weight of the drink change?

_____

_____

5. Based on what we have seen, can you predict the total weight of a solution or mixture after adding ingredients? If so, how?

_____

_____

_____

_____

_____

 **Explore 2**

6. **Problem:** A student made lemonade with water, lemon juice, and sugar. Before she made lemonade, she found the weight of the cup of water and the sugar, but she forgot to find the weight of the lemon juice. Using the following weights, determine the weight of the lemon juice. **The cup of water = 102 g, sugar = 1 g, and the cup of lemonade drink = 107 g.** Be sure to show your work and explain your answer.

Explore 2

Sweet Tea
Claim-Evidence-Reasoning

Prompt

Write a scientific explanation describing how the total weight of a mixture can be predicted.

Claim:

_____

_____

_____

Evidence:

_____

_____

_____

Reasoning:

_____

_____

_____

_____

_____

_____

Explore 3

What's My Weight?

Directions:

1. Place a cup with baking soda and a cup with vinegar upright inside a bag. Be sure to not spill them.

2. Completely seal the bag.

3. Place the entire bag onto the pan of the triple beam balance. Make sure no part of the bag is hanging off the edge of the pan.

4. Weigh the system and record the weight.

5. Spill the contents of the cups inside the bag without opening it.

6. Record any observations.

7. Weigh the bag and its contents again. Make sure no part of the bag is hanging off the edge of the pan.

8. Set the bag aside and repeat this process with the following mixtures: baking soda and lemon juice, and effervescent heartburn tablet and water.

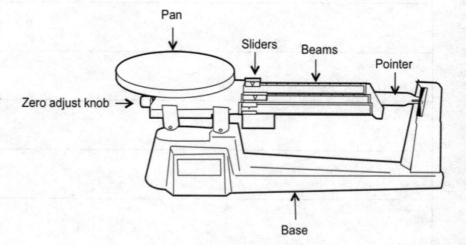

Mixtures	Observations	Weight Before (g)	Weight After (g)
Baking soda and vinegar	I saw a reaction when they came together	both sides were the same	the side a reaction weighed less
Baking soda and lemon juice	there was a reaction with bubbles and not air	same mass	little change to weight but still same mass
Effervescent heartburn tablet and water	it was a reaction with big bubbles were there for a whirl	same mass	it had a big mass change

Explore 3

9. Use the data you have collected to create a double-bar graph that displays your results. Be sure to include a title, a key, and specific labels for each axis.

Title_____

Key

10. What patterns did you notice in your graph?

_____

_____

_____

_____

 **Explore 3**

11. Chemical reactions cause new substances to be formed. What does your graph tell you about the weight of a mixture before and after a chemical reaction takes place?

_____

_____

_____

_____

_____

 **Explore 3**

What's My Weight?
Claim-Evidence-Reasoning

Prompt

Using a scientific explanation, describe if the weight of a mixture will change after going through a chemical reaction. State your claim and provide specific evidence and reasoning for your answer.

Claim:

_____

_____

_____

Evidence:

_____

_____

_____

Reasoning:

_____

_____

_____

_____

_____

_____

Linking Literacy
Pre-Reading

3-2-1 Notes

Before you read: Complete the table below.

3 **3:** Facts You Know about States of Matter	• _____ _____ • _____ _____ • _____ _____
2 **2:** Examples of How We See States of Matter Change	• _____ _____ • _____ _____
1 **1:** Question You Still Have about the States of Matter	• _____ _____ _____

Linking Literacy
During-Reading

Main Ideas and Details

While you read: Look for details in the text that give more information about the three main ideas listed below. Write four details for every main idea.

Text Topic: **Matter can change states.**

Page	Main Idea:	Detail 1	Detail 2
	Cooling air can cause condensation.		
		Detail 3	Detail 4

Linking Literacy
During-Reading

Page	Main Idea:	Detail 1	Detail 2
	A change in temperature can cause a change in state.		
		Detail 3	Detail 4

Page	Main Idea:	Detail 1	Detail 2
	Particles of matter behave differently when heated or cooled.		
		Detail 3	Detail 4

Name: _____ Date: _____

Linking Literacy
Post-Reading

Anchor Chart

List three main facts you want to include on your anchor chart.

_____

_____

_____

Use the space below to plan how your anchor chart will look before creating the final copy.

Reading Science

Signs of Chemical Change

1. Hundreds of years ago, early scientists began to systematically explore the way that different compounds behave when mixed together. They mixed many, many substances to see what would happen. They made observations of the properties of the starting compounds and what happened when the substances first touched one another. They ran tests on the mixtures to see if the chemical properties had changed. They took careful notes and shared them with other scientists.

2. When many observations were put together, scientists noticed patterns that led to a set of rules on how to tell when a chemical change had happened. Here are the five rules early scientists developed:

   • There is a production of light.
   • There is a production of a precipitate.
   • There is a production of gas.
   • There is an unexpected color change.
   • There is a change in temperature.

   Even though these rules are old, they are still used today to determine when a chemical change happens. Each of these relies on a property that can be directly seen or measured in an experiment. This is called **empirical** evidence.

3. Maria had several compounds in the lab. She wanted to find out if a new substance is formed when certain pairs of them are mixed, so she designed an experiment to investigate. Maria used the five rules to determine if a chemical change had occurred.

4. Maria developed a procedure that she used for each mixture. First, she measured equal amounts of each of the two compounds to be mixed and put one of them into a test tube. She examined them carefully and wrote what she observed in her notebook. Watching closely, she put the second compound into the test tube, swirling to mix the two substances together. She put the test tube into the rack, let it sit for one minute, and then recorded her observations.

5. Here are the mixtures Maria tested and the observations she made:

   A. Two clear liquids began to glow with a yellow light after mixing.
   B. Two clear liquids were mixed, but they did not look any different afterward.
   C. A piece of metal was dropped into a clear liquid. Before long, small bubbles began to float to the surface.
   D. A clear liquid was added to a dark blue liquid. The resulting mixture was light blue.
   E. A clear liquid was added to a pale yellow liquid, forming a white powder that settled on the bottom.
   F. A clear liquid was poured onto a white powder. Immediately, it fizzed and foamed. After one minute, the bubbles were gone, and only a clear liquid remained.

6. After the tests were complete, Maria reviewed her observations and analyzed her results to see if a chemical change had occurred. Soon, Maria knew which combinations had produced a new substance. Do you?

Reading Science

1. Identify the flaw in the way that Maria set up her experiment.

    A.   She did not take pictures.

    B.   She did not wait long enough.

    C.   She did not measure the temperature.

    D.   She did not mix the substances well enough.

2. Which of these describes Maria making an observation?

    A.   Maria measured the compounds.

    B.   Maria let the test tube sit for one minute.

    C.   Maria wrote her results in her lab notebook.

    D.   Maria saw that bubbles formed on the metal in mixture C.

Reading Science

3. What is the best summary of this passage?

A. Early scientists studied the way substances behaved when they were combined. They developed rules to identify when a chemical change occurred. Maria used those rules to create an experimental procedure and test six mixtures.

B. Maria was curious about how several compounds acted when mixed. She put them into test tubes and swirled them together. She could tell if a chemical change had occurred by watching for signs such as bubbles or light.

C. Maria mixed compounds together to test for chemical change. One mixture produced light, two mixtures had bubbles, two mixtures had changes of color, and one mixture did not change.

D. You can tell if a chemical change has occurred because there will be a production of light, gas, or a precipitate, or there will be a change in color or temperature.

4. Using Maria's results, determine how many mixtures produced a new substance.

A. 3

B. 4

C. 5

D. 6

5. Which is the best definition of **empirical** in paragraph 2?

A. Can be seen or measured

B. From a currently used procedure

C. Collected in an old, reliable method

D. Related to whether a chemical change has occurred

Reading Science

6. Maria made a mistake in the analysis of her results. Which of the following conclusions is incorrect?

    A.   A chemical change occurred in mixture A, because there was a production of light.

    B.   A chemical change occurred in mixture D, because there was a color change.

    C.   A chemical change occurred in mixture E, because there was a production of a precipitate.

    D.   A chemical change occurred in mixture F, because there was a production of a gas.

Name: _____ Date: _____

Open-Ended Response

1. Your friend is wondering if an ice cube has more mass before or after it melts. What would you tell him?

_____

_____

_____

_____

_____

2. You weigh a small tablet and a cup of liquid. You place the tablet into the liquid and it begins to bubble until you can no longer see it. You weigh the final mixture and it is lighter than the original ingredients. What do you think happened to make it weigh less? How could you investigate your idea?

_____

_____

_____

_____

_____

3. Everyone likes hot chocolate! Describe how you would make hot chocolate. Explain how you could calculate the final weight of your hot chocolate. What information would you need?

_____

_____

_____

_____

_____

Claim-Evidence-Reasoning

Scenario

A group of Boy Scouts went on a camping trip over the weekend. One evening, they made a campfire. The next morning, they noticed the logs were gone and only a pile of ashes was left. When they got back home, they decided to test what happened on a smaller scale, with the help of their science teacher. Instead of using large logs, they used small sticks in a closed, fireproof container. When the sticks were finished burning, only ashes were left. Their data is shown in the table below.

	Description	Mass
Before Burning	Sticks	25 grams
After Burning	Ashes	25 grams

Prompt

Write a scientific explanation describing how the amount of matter in the container changed after burning.

Claim:

_____

_____

_____

_____

Claim-Evidence-Reasoning

Evidence:

_____

_____

_____

_____

_____

_____

Reasoning:

_____

_____

_____

_____

_____

_____

_____

_____

_____

_____

_____

Properties of Matter

Name: _____

Date: _____

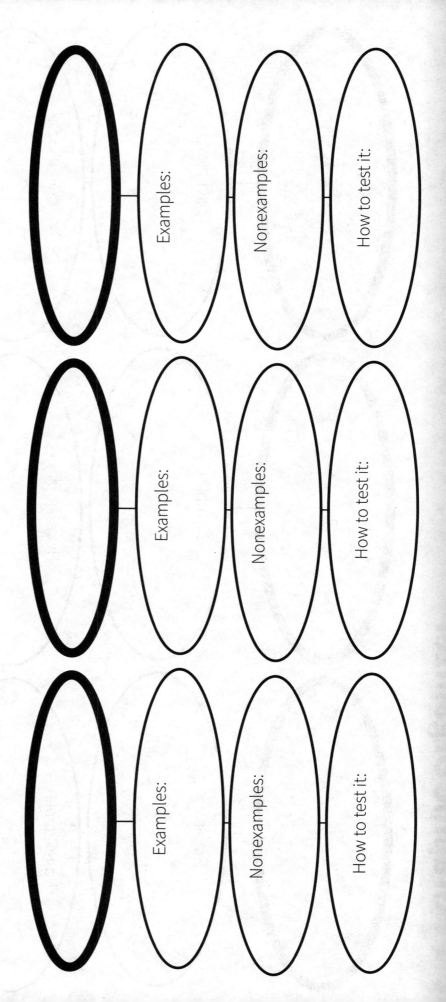

Graphic Organizer

Properties of Matter

Directions: In each bolded oval, record a physical property that you could test or observe. Then, list in the connected ovals examples, nonexamples, and how each property is tested.

Examples:

Nonexamples:

How to test it:

Examples:

Nonexamples:

How to test it:

Examples:

Nonexamples:

How to test it:

Graphic Organizer

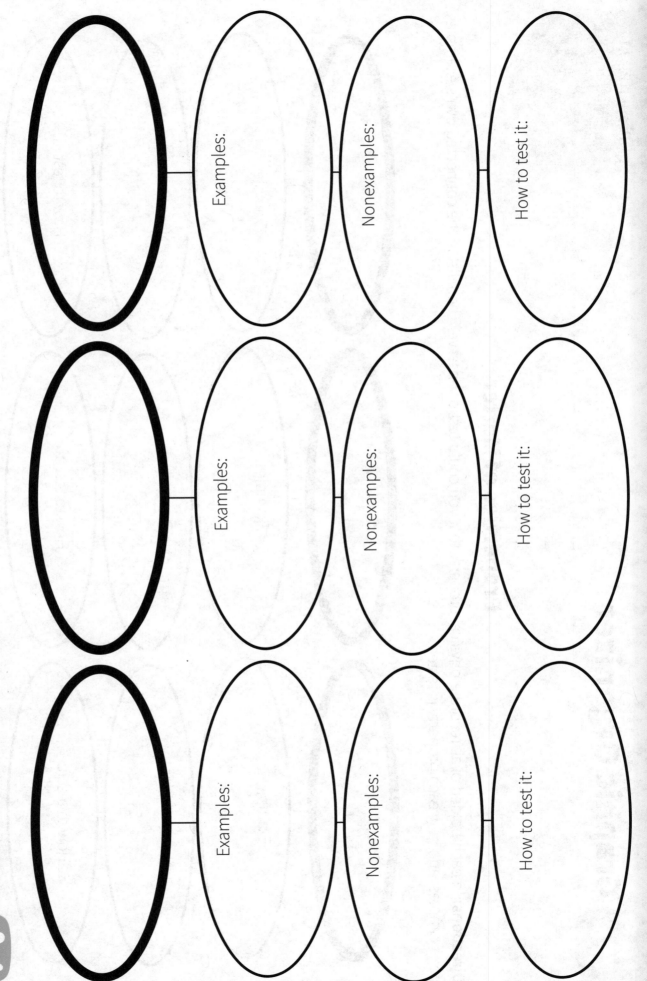

Examples:

Nonexamples:

How to test it:

Examples:

Nonexamples:

How to test it:

Examples:

Nonexamples:

How to test it:

Graphic Organizer

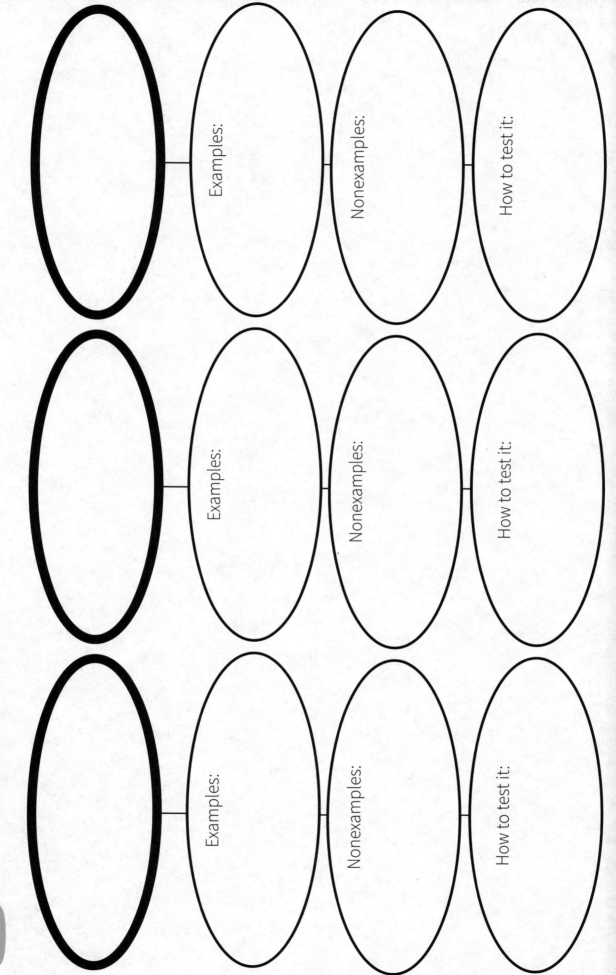

Examples:

Nonexamples:

How to test it:

Examples:

Nonexamples:

How to test it:

Examples:

Nonexamples:

How to test it:

Explore 1

Figuring Out Physical Properties

Our Driving Question

Which materials conduct electricity or heat, are attracted to a magnet, and reflect light?

What We Need

1 Metal spoon

1 Iron nail

1 Wooden craft stick

1 Plastic spoon

1 Aluminum foil sheet

_____

_____

Procedure

1. Your group will be testing five objects to see if they can conduct electricity or heat (thermal energy), reflect light, or be attracted to a magnet.

2. Discuss which materials you will use to test each property of matter (electricity, thermal conductivity, magnetism, and reflectivity). Record the materials you will need on the lines above.

3. A student from each group will gather the materials needed for testing as well as a bag of objects to be tested.

4. On the next page, record your plan for how you will test each physical property using the materials you gathered.

5. You have 15 minutes to test your objects.

6. Record all observations in your data table. In each column, write "Yes" if the material has the physical property. Write "No" if it does not have the physical property.

7. Answer the reflection question.

Explore 1

Plan

Electrical conductivity:

_____

_____

_____

Thermal (heat) conductivity:

_____

_____

_____

Response to magnetism:

_____

_____

_____

Reflectivity:

_____

_____

_____

Explore 1

Data and Results

	Electrical Conductor	Attracted to a Magnet	Thermal Conductor	Reflects Light
Metal Spoon				
Iron Nail				
Aluminum Foil				
Wooden Craft Stick				
Plastic Spoon				

Review the data from the table. What are some patterns you notice about physical properties?

_____

_____

_____

_____

Name: _____ Date: _____

Explore 1

Figuring Out Physical Properties
Claim-Evidence-Reasoning

Prompt

A mystery material is an electrical and thermal conductor, reflects light, and is magnetic. Write a scientific explanation describing what the material could be.

Claim:

_____

_____

_____

Evidence:

_____

_____

_____

Reasoning:

_____

_____

_____

_____

_____

_____

Explore 2

Solubility

Driving Question
Which of the unknown substances dissolve in water, and how can that help me identify them?

What We Need
1 Graduated cylinder (per group)

1 Pair of safety goggles (per student)

5 Stir sticks (per group)

1 tsp Instant coffee (per group)

1 tsp Cinnamon (per group)

1 tsp White sand (per group)

1 tsp Cornstarch (per group)

1 tsp Table salt (per group)

5 8oz Clear plastic cups (per group)

250 mL Water (per group)

Directions
1. Take a moment to look at the data table on the next page.
2. Observe Substance 1. Record the color and particle size (fine, small, medium, large, very large) in the table.
3. Feel Substance 1. Be careful to not spill the substance, since all of the substance will be needed later. Record the texture in the table.
4. Observe Substances 2–5. Record the color, particle size, and texture in the table.
5. Label each clear plastic cup with a number, "Substance 1" through "Substance 5."
6. Fill each cup with 50 mL of water, using the graduated cylinder.
7. In the cup labeled Substance 1, pour in a teaspoon of Substance 1. Stir for 15 seconds.

Explore 2

8. Repeat the previous step for each substance.

9. Record your observations in your data table.

10. Use the Clue Card and your observations to identify each mystery substance. Write the name of the substance in the blank at the top of the correct column.

11. Answer the reflection questions below.

Data and Observations

	Substance 1 _____	Substance 2 _____	Substance 3 _____	Substance 4 _____	Substance 5 _____
Color					
Texture					
Particle Size					
Soluble in Water?					

Reflection Questions

1. Using the data you collected, which substances were similar in particle size?

_____

_____

_____

_____

Explore 2

2. How do you know if a substance is soluble in water?

_____

_____

_____

3. How do you know if a substance is not soluble in water?

_____

_____

_____

4. How does solubility help you identify substances?

_____

_____

_____

5. Describe how the observations you recorded on your data chart help identify materials based on their properties.

_____

_____

_____

 **Explore 2**

Solubility
Claim-Evidence-Reasoning

Prompt:

Using scientific reasoning, write a scientific explanation for the identity of substance 3.

Claim:

_____

_____

_____

Evidence:

_____

_____

_____

Reasoning:

_____

_____

_____

_____

_____

_____

Explore 3

What's the Matter?

Directions

1. Select a matter card. Do not share the card with the others in your group.

2. Group members may ask up to 21 yes-or-no questions to try to figure out what is on the card. (Each guess of the card takes away from the 21 questions.)

3. The questions can only be about the physical properties (size, shape, hardness, color, reflectivity, electrical conductivity, thermal conductivity, response to magnetic forces, solubility, texture, etc.).

4. You can use your Graphic Organizer as a reference if you need help.

5. If the object is guessed, another student may choose a different card and start over. If the card was not guessed after 21 questions, share what was on the card, and another student may choose a different card to continue the game.

6. After the game is over, select four cards that could be grouped together based on a physical property they all share.

7. When the other groups are ready, take turns looking at one another's grouping and guessing what property was used to classify the materials.

8. Complete the data table below. List each of the four objects you are grouping together. Beside each object, list the physical properties each has in the second column. Circle the property the four types of matter have in common.

9. If time allows, repeat the grouping game by choosing another four objects that have a physical property in common.

Type of Matter	Physical Properties

 **Explore 3**

Reflection Questions

1. Which physical property do the types of matter you chose have in common?

_____

_____

_____

_____

2. Are there other common physical properties? _____
   List the types of matter and the properties they have in common.

_____

_____

_____

_____

_____

_____

3. Did anyone else use a different property to group the same four types of matter together? _____
   What physical property did they use?

_____

_____

_____

_____

_____

Name: _____ Date: _____

Linking Literacy
Pre- and Post-Reading

Properties of Matter KWL

K	W	L
What I Know	**What I Want to Know**	**What I Learned**

Linking Literacy
During-Reading

Properties of Matter Concept Definition Map

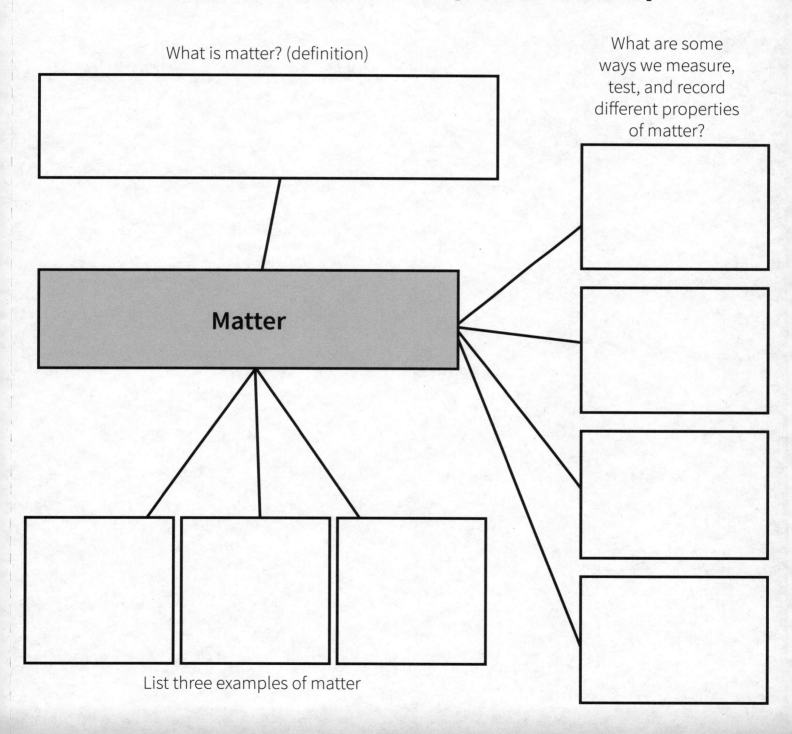

What is matter? (definition)

What are some ways we measure, test, and record different properties of matter?

Matter

List three examples of matter

Reading Science

An Unusual Material

1. Here is a riddle. What is made of sand and can often be seen through? Need a hint? It is fragile, but also very strong. Did you answer, "glass"? If you did, then you would be correct!

2. Yes, glass is made from sand. To make glass, sand is melted. Then, a few ingredients are added to the liquid. Finally, it is cooled. Different ingredients are added to make different colors and types of glass. Artists with torches and metal rods can blow and shape the liquid glass into beautiful creations that become solid after they cool.

3. However, it does not take a glass artist to create glass. Nature can also form glass. Volcanoes produce temperatures that are hot enough to melt sand. When the liquid sand cools, it becomes solid, volcanic glass. This glass is called obsidian. Obsidian is usually black in color and is **opaque**. This means you cannot see through it. Obsidian is very shiny. If it is broken, the edges are sharp, like any piece of broken glass. Long ago, people used this natural glass to make razor-sharp arrowheads.

4. Glass has other interesting properties, as well. It has no specific melting point. The melting point varies, depending on how the glass is made, and it changes characteristics, depending on how fast it is cooled. One example of how the speed of cooling affects glass is the Prince Rupert's drop. A Prince Rupert's drop is created when molten glass is dropped into very cold water. This creates a teardrop shape with a long tail. The rounded end is very hard and can be hit with a hammer without breaking. If you hit the tail, however, watch out! The entire piece of glass will explode!

5. Glass does not conduct electricity, but it does conduct heat. You can observe the heat conductivity of glass by putting your hand against a window on a cold day. Even though it might be warm inside the house, the window will be cold. The window allows the warm air from inside the house to move to the colder air outdoors. This leaves the glass feeling cold. Windows can make it harder for your house to remain at an even temperature because of this heat conductivity. Some windows are insulated to better conserve energy. These windows are made using two panes of glass with air sandwiched in between the panes. Having insulated windows can help save money on heating and cooling your house.

6. People have found many ways to use glass because of its interesting properties. Aside from windows, glass can be shaped to form lenses through which light can pass. The lenses refract, or bend, light. These lenses can be found in eyeglasses, cameras, telescopes, and many other things. Glass can also be coated with silver or aluminum to make mirrors that reflect light. Glass can be formed into jars and bottles that package food and drinks. This packaging can be recycled (melted and used again).

7. The next time you drink soda from a glass bottle or look out your window, think about the many amazing properties of glass!

Reading Science

1. Why is glass useful for making eyeglasses?

    A. Glass is fragile, yet strong.

    B. Glass changes characteristics, depending on how it is cooled.

    C. Glass shaped into a lens can bend light that passes through it.

    D. Glass coated with aluminum or silver reflects light.

2. Which of these is a physical property of glass?

    A. It conducts electricity.

    B. It conducts heat.

    C. It cannot be melted.

    D. All of the above.

3. Which diagram shows the change that produces glass?

    1. Solid → Liquid → Solid

    2. Liquid → Solid → Gas

    3. Gas → Solid → Liquid

    4. Solid → Liquid → Gas

    A. 1

    B. 2

    C. 3

    D. 4

Reading Science

4. Which of these would be **opaque** (paragraph 3)?

   A. A window

   B. A clear glass bottle

   C. A mirror

   D. A fishbowl

5. A Prince Rupert's drop is an illustration of which characteristic of glass?

   A. Glass has different qualities, depending upon how quickly it cools.

   B. Glass conducts heat.

   C. Glass is made of sand.

   D. Glass can be created by humans or nature.

Name: _____ Date: _____

Open-Ended Response

1. Name three things that are attracted to a magnet and three that are not. Explain why the items you selected will be attracted to a magnet or not.

_____

_____

_____

_____

_____

2. You want to see which substances dissolve in water. You test sugar, salt, and pepper. Explain which of these substances will dissolve in water and which will not.

_____

_____

_____

_____

_____

3. You and your friends are at the park on a sunny day. You are playing on the slide. As you slide down, the hot metal slide burns your legs. Explain why this happened and why you did not burn your hands when you climbed up the rope ladder.

_____

_____

_____

_____

 Claim-Evidence-Reasoning

Properties of Matter

Scenario

After a rainfall, Katie and Bryan found a piece of metal on the playground at school. The Sun was shining brightly now, and the light reflected off the silver metal. Bryan picked it up. It felt warm and wet. They discussed the possible metals it could be. They narrowed it down to three kinds: iron, copper, or aluminum. They carried it into the classroom and found it was not attracted to a magnet and did conduct electricity. Use your knowledge of physical properties to help them figure out what kind of metal they found.

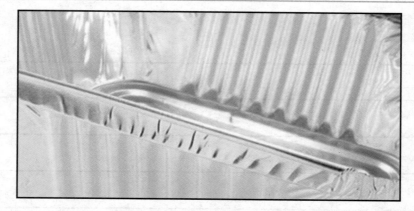

Metal	Iron	Copper	Aluminum
Color	Gray	Yellow orange	Shiny silver
Electrical Conductivity	Yes	Yes	Yes
Thermal Conductivity	Yes	Yes	Yes
Magnetism	Magnetic	Nonmagnetic	Nonmagnetic
Reflectivity	Reflective	Reflective	Reflective
Solubility	No	No	No

Claim-Evidence-Reasoning

Claim:

_____

_____

_____

_____

Evidence:

_____

_____

_____

_____

_____

_____

Reasoning:

_____

_____

_____

_____

_____

Mixtures

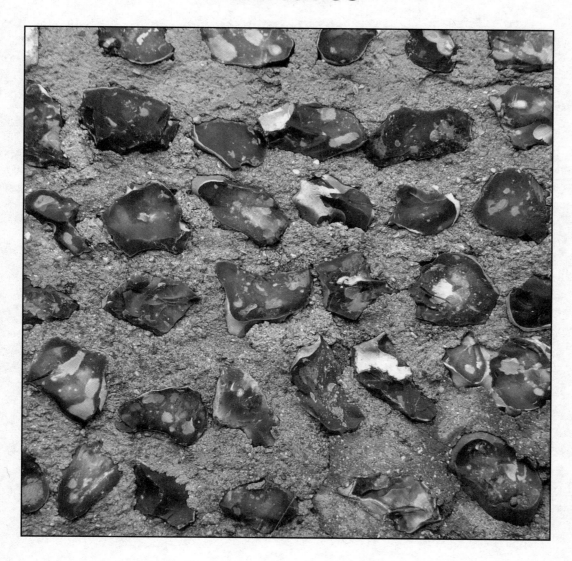

Graphic Organizer

Physical vs. Chemical

Directions: Describe a physical change and list what you could observe as evidence of a physical change. Describe a chemical change and list what you could observe as evidence of a chemical change. Then give examples of each.

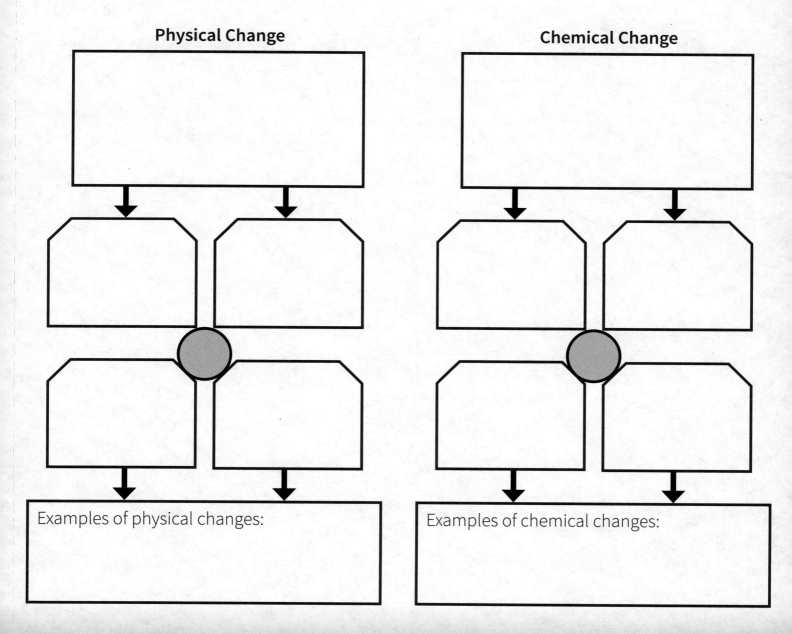

Explore 1

Expect the Unexpected

Driving Question
Can we mix things to create a new substance?

What we need
1 Long stirring stick (per group)

1 Thermometer (per group)

2 Large clear plastic cups (per group)

1 Pair of goggles (per student)

2 Paper towels (per group)

1 tsp. Yeast (per group)

60 mL Hydrogen peroxide (per group)

1 tsp Baking soda (per group)

60 mL Distilled white vinegar (per group)

Procedure
1. Be sure to follow all safety rules.

    - When working in a lab, it is extremely important that you do not taste any of the materials, even if you think it is edible.

    - You should wear your goggles the entire time, because groups around you may be conducting tests, even if you are not.

    - Never play around in the lab, as this could cause accidents and injuries.

    - If you are wearing a shirt with long sleeves, roll them up, and tie back your hair if it is long.

    - Try to prevent the materials from getting on your skin or clothing.

    - Wash your hands with soap and water if you get something on them.

Explore 1

2. Pour the hydrogen peroxide into a cup. Place the thermometer in the liquid. Let it sit a minute until it is stabilized, then record the temperature on the data table. Remove the thermometer.

3. Predict if the temperature will increase, decrease, or stay the same when the yeast is added. Record your prediction.

4. Pour the yeast into the liquid in the cup. Observe what happens. Record your observations on the data table.

5. Place the thermometer in the mixture. Let it stabilize, then read and record the temperature again.

6. Repeat these steps two more times for a total of three trials.

7. Pour the vinegar into the other cup. Place the thermometer in the liquid. Let it sit a minute until it is stabilized, then record the temperature on the data table. Remove the thermometer.

8. Predict if the temperature will increase, decrease, or stay the same when the baking soda is added. Record your prediction.

9. Pour the baking soda into the liquid in the cup. Observe what happens. Record your observations on the second data table.

10. Place the thermometer in the mixture. Let it stabilize, then read and record the temperature again.

11. Repeat these steps two more times for a total of three trials.

Data and Observations
When the yeast is added to the hydrogen peroxide, I think the temperature will

_____

_____

_____

Explore 1

Hydrogen Peroxide and Yeast			
	Temperature **before** Adding Yeast	Temperature **after** Adding Yeast	Observations and Notes
Trial 1			
Trial 2			
Trial 3			

When the baking soda is added to the vinegar, I think the temperature will

_____

Vinegar and Baking Soda			
	Temperature **before** Adding Baking Soda	Temperature **after** Adding Baking Soda	Observations and Notes
Trial 1			
Trial 2			
Trial 3			

Explore 1

Reflection

What did both tests have in common?

_____

_____

_____

_____

Was a new substance formed? How do you know?

_____

_____

_____

_____

Why do you think you tested each mixture three times?

_____

_____

_____

_____

Explore 1

Expect the Unexpected
Claim-Evidence-Reasoning

Prompt

Write a scientific explanation that describes whether or not these two mixtures, hydrogen peroxide mixed with yeast, and vinegar mixed with baking soda, caused a new substance to form. State your claim, and provide specific evidence and reasoning for your answer.

Claim:

_____

_____

Evidence:

_____

_____

_____

Reasoning:

_____

_____

_____

_____

Explore 2

Reaction or Not?

Our Driving Question

Does the mixing of two or more substances result in the formation of a new substance?

Procedure

1. Follow the directions on the card at each station.

2. Record all data and observations in the table below. Determine whether a new substance was formed, based on your observations.

3. Be sure to repeat each test two times, for a total of three trials each.

4. Always clean up your station before moving on to the next one.

Mixture	Trial 1	Trial 2	Trial 3	Did a New Substance Form?
1: Lemon juice and chalk				
2: Warm milk and vinegar				
3: Water, powdered drink mix, and sugar				
4: Water and gravel				

Explore 2

1. Did you mix two or more substances at each station?

_____

_____

2. Did a new substance form each time?

_____

_____

3. How could you tell if a new substance had formed? What did you observe?

_____

_____

_____

_____

4. What occurred that caused a new substance to form?

_____

_____

_____

5. Does a chemical reaction always occur when two or more substances are mixed? How do you know?

_____

_____

_____

_____

6. When two or more substances are mixed, a _____ _____ forms if a _____ _____ has occurred.

Explore 2

Reaction or Not?
Claim-Evidence-Reasoning

Prompt

Write a scientific explanation describing if the mixing of two or more substances results in the formation of a new substance. State your claim, and provide specific evidence and reasoning for your answer.

Claim:

_____

_____

_____

Evidence:

_____

_____

_____

Reasoning:

_____

_____

_____

_____

_____

Explore 3

My Mixtures Investigation

Plan It!

Our questions: (Remember to make sure you choose a question that is testable!)

_____

_____

_____

Our ideas for answering our question:

(Remember to make an observation: What do I see, hear, feel, smell, or taste?)

- Make a model
- Take a survey (I can ask my family and friends a question.)
- Measure and collect data
- Design an experiment

What materials will we need?

_____

_____

_____

What procedure will we follow?

_____

_____

_____

Explore 3

Test It!

Data and observations:

Explore 3

Wrap It Up!

Rewrite your original question:

_____

_____

_____

_____

Write a **claim** that answers your question:

_____

_____

_____

_____

What **evidence** did you gather that supports your claim?

_____

_____

_____

Provide **reasoning** that connects your evidence to your claim:

_____

_____

_____

_____

Linking Literacy
During-Reading

Claim and Evidence

Evidence

Evidence

Claim

Chemical changes involve changes
to the physical and chemical properties
of a substance.

Evidence

Evidence

Name: _____

Date: _____

Linking Literacy
Post-Reading

Chemical Change

For each combination of ingredients, record the change that will occur when the ingredients are combined.

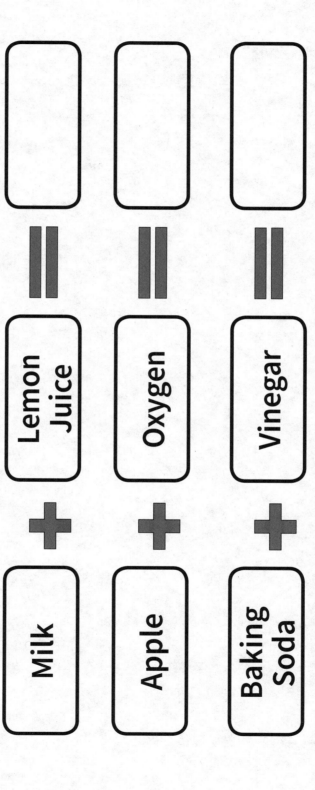

Milk + Lemon Juice = [ ]

Apple + Oxygen = [ ]

Baking Soda + Vinegar = [ ]

Describe ways to determine if a chemical change has occurred.

_____

_____

_____

Reading Science

Name: _____ Date: _____

Jeremiah's Science Project

1. Jeremiah was worried. Yesterday in science class, his teacher passed out science project topics. Jeremiah wanted to get something cool, such as chemical reactions, because he really wanted to make a volcano. The teacher handed Jeremiah his topic. He read the piece of paper that said, "matter changing states." "How boring is *that*?" thought Jeremiah.

2. On Saturday, Jeremiah talked to his parents about his topic. He knew he would try his best, even if nothing could explode. Jeremiah started digging into his research.

3. Jeremiah knew he had to show that there is not a change in mass when a substance changes states. He found a credible website explaining more about changing states of matter. He read on, and his face lit up as an idea came to him. He soon knew what he would do!

4. On Monday, he set out his supplies, as this was the day he would share his research with the class. He had a ziplock bag, some water, an Alka-Seltzer tablet, and a **balance** used for weighing. First, he measured the mass of the ziplock bag with the water. After that, he measured the mass of the tablet. Finally, Jeremiah added up the total mass of the bag, water, and tablet together.

5. "And now for the fun part," thought Jeremiah, with a twinkle in his eye. He placed the tablet into the plastic bag. The class watched what happened. The water in the bag began to bubble, then the bubbling stopped. Jeremiah measured the mass of the bag. The mass was the same as the total starting mass of the bag, water, and tablet.

6. "It may not be as exciting as a volcano," thought Jeremiah, "but at least I got a little sizzle!"

Reading Science

1. Which of the following definitions of **balance** best fits the way the word is used in paragraph 4?

   A.   The state of having your weight spread equally so that you do not fall

   B.   An instrument for weighing

   C.   The ability to move or to remain in a position without losing control

   D.   Something left over; a remainder

2. Which sentence best supports the idea that no matter what reaction or change in properties occurs, the total weight of the substances does not change?

   A.   *Jeremiah knew he had to show that there is not a change in mass when a substance changes states.*

   B.   *Finally, Jeremiah measured the total mass of the bag, water, and tablet.*

   C.   *The mass was the same as the total starting mass of the bag, water, and tablet together.*

   D.   *He placed the tablet into the plastic bag.*

3. From the sentence, *He knew he would try his best, even if nothing could explode*, the reader can conclude–

   A.   Jeremiah was determined.

   B.   Jeremiah was upset about his topic.

   C.   Jeremiah would make a volcano for his project.

   D.   Jeremiah was excited.

4. What was Jeremiah's problem in the story?

    A.   He did not know what "matter changing states" meant.

    B.   He did not know how to make a volcano science project.

    C.   He did not like his science project topic.

    D.   He had trouble researching his topic.

5. This story is written in–

    A.   first person, from Jeremiah's point of view.

    B.   third person, from a narrator's point of view.

    C.   second person, from the teacher's point of view.

    D.   third person, from Jeremiah's parents' point of view.

6. What is the best summary of this selection?

    A.   Jeremiah hoped to get "chemical reactions" for his science project. He really wanted to make a volcano for his project. He was mad that he did not get that topic.

    B.   Jeremiah's science class was working on science projects. Jeremiah got the topic "matter changing states." He was excited to research his topic. He found a cool experiment to conduct for the class.

    C.   Jeremiah showed his class an experiment. He set out all his supplies. He showed that even though a reaction happened, the mass of the substances did not change. He was excited about the sizzle when adding the tablet.

    D.   At first, Jeremiah was disappointed with his science project topic, "matter changing states," but he soon realized he could still make it fun. He showed the class a cool experiment that included a little excitement, after all.

 Open-Ended Response

1. Fruit punch is made by mixing a flavored powder with water. When you add the mix to the water, the properties of the mixture change. Is this a chemical reaction? Explain why or why not.

_____

_____

_____

_____

_____

2. Maggie is making pancakes. She notices tiny bubbles popping in the batter as they cook in the skillet. Is the pancake batter changing physically or chemically as it cooks?

_____

_____

_____

_____

_____

3. Luke's iron garden tools were left outside over the winter. When found, they appeared dirty with spots of a reddish-brown, flaky substance. Was this a physical or chemical change? How do you know?

_____

_____

_____

_____

_____

Claim-Evidence-Reasoning

Mixtures

Scenario

Luke was making himself a cold drink with some water and lime drink mix. His mom was making a snack with cheese and tomatoes. His dad was taking an antacid by mixing it with water. Luke noticed how everyone in his family was mixing things and causing changes. He wondered if his family was actually creating anything new.

Item 1	Item 2	Result
Effervescent antacid	**Water**	
Mozzarella cheese	**Tomato**	
Lime drink mix	**Water**	

Claim-Evidence-Reasoning

Prompt

Write a scientific explanation that describes which mixture caused a chemical reaction. State your evidence and reasoning to support your claim.

Claim:

_____

_____

_____

_____

Evidence:

_____

_____

_____

_____

_____

_____

Reasoning:

_____

_____

_____

_____

_____

_____

Name: _____

Date: _____

California Instructional Segment
Mission Log

Mission Log

Anchoring Phenomena

How can you develop a system to help grow and sustain plant and human life on a foreign planet?

Mission Briefing

You are part of a team who will be colonizing Mars. Your job is to design a closed system to grow plants with limited resources, including water, soil, and nutrients. Keep in mind there is no water available on the planet and the air on Mars is very different from the air on Earth.

- What matter do plants need to grow?
- How does matter move within an ecosystem?
- How does energy move within an ecosystem?

California Instructional Segment
Mission Log

Class Mission Log

Information Gained

Matter and Energy in Plants

Think about how a plant's needs are met on Earth. Complete the plant section of the chart below.

Connection to Mission

Matter and Energy in Plants

Think about how a plant's needs could be met on Mars. Complete the plant section of the chart below.

	How Is the Need Met on Earth?	How Could the Need Be Met on Mars?
	Plant	Plant
Food		
Water		
Air		
Shelter		

California Instructional Segment
Mission Log

Class Mission Log

Information Gained

Connection to Mission

Food Webs

How does energy from the Sun flow from one organism to another?

Food Webs

What will be the biggest difference between a food web on Earth and a food web on Mars?

Ecosystems

What are some components of an ecosystem on Earth?

Ecosystems

What components of an ecosystem will we have to duplicate on Mars?

Matter Cycles

When an organism dies, what happens to the remains?

Matter Cycles

How will organic waste be used on Mars to benefit the project?

California Instructional Segment
Mission Log

Class Mission Log

Information Gained	Connection to Mission
Energy Transfer	**Energy Transfer**
How is energy transferred?	Will the energy from the Sun be different on Mars than on Earth?
Earth's Systems Interactions	**Earth's Systems Interactions**
What are some systems on Earth?	What systems will need to be recreated on Mars?

Name: _____ Date: _____

California Instructional Segment
Action Plan

Action Plan

Using the limited resources available, plan and design a system that will grow and sustain plant and human life on a Martian colony.

Here's what we know:

- Plants need water, air, and sunlight.

- Humans need air, food, water, and shelter.

- Humans and plants depend on each other to meet their needs.

- Resources will need to be conserved or reused because no new supplies will be sent to Mars.

- Organisms on Mars will need protection from the radiation of the Sun, cold temperatures, and extreme weather conditions, such as dust storms and high winds.

California Instructional Segment

Action Plan

Take Action

Plan your design.

What Features Will It Need?	How Will All the Parts Interact?	How Will the Limited Resources Be Conserved or Reused?

California Instructional Segment

Action Plan

Take Action

Draw and label a plan of your system.

Matter and Energy in Plants

Graphic Organizer

A Recipe for Growth

Directions: Describe how a plant acquires the material needed for growth.

Plant Part	Ingredient It Absorbs
Leaves	
Roots	

	+	**= New Plant Matter**

 **Explore 1**

Growing Plants without Soil

Our Driving Question

Can plants grow with only water and air?

What We Need

1 Plastic bag

1 Paper towel

3–5 Seeds

Water

Tape

Stapler

Directions

1. Fold a paper towel so that it is the same size as the inside of the plastic bag.

2. Place the dry, folded towel in the bag. Check to be sure that the bag will zip.

3. Use a stapler to place a row of staples dividing the top half from the bottom half of the bag. The staples should not overlap. If you are using small seeds, the staples should be closer together so that when you add the seeds they will not fall into the bottom half of the bag.

4. Add three to five seeds to the bag (or more, if directed by your teacher) so that they are supported above the row of staples.

5. Add water to the bag very slowly, allowing it to soak completely into the paper towel. Continue slowly adding water until you have a little reservoir of water about 2 cm deep at the bottom of the bag.

6. Zip the bag closed so that nothing can get in or out.

7. Use the digital scale to measure the weight of your prepared bag. Record the starting weight. Handle the bag gently while completing this step, so as not to disturb the setup.

8. With the zip side on top, tape the bag to a window or clip it to the supported twine as directed by your teacher.

9. Make daily observations of what is happening inside your bag by drawing and describing on your data table for two weeks. Be careful to not disturb the plant. Leave the bag taped to the window or pinned to the twine at all times while measuring and observing. **Do not open the bag to observe!**

10. At the end of the two-week period, use the digital scale to measure the final weight of your bag. Record it.

11. Answer the reflection questions.

Name: _____ Date: _____

 # Explore 1

Growing Plants without Soil

Claim-Evidence-Reasoning

Prompt

Write a scientific explanation about where the new plant matter came from.

Claim:

_____

_____

Evidence:

_____

_____

_____

_____

Reasoning:

_____

_____

_____

_____

_____

_____

Name: _____

Date: _____

Linking Literacy
Pre-Reading

What Plants Need Comic Strip

Think about what you already know about plants and what they need to grow. Use the space below to create a comic strip that explains what plants need. Provide a caption for each frame of your comic strip on the lines provided.

Name: _____ Date: _____

Linking Literacy
During-Reading

Describe with an Image

Directions: Write a description for each word below. Draw a picture to explain your description.

Describe photosynthesis.	Draw an image.

Describe hydroponics.	Draw an image.

Describe epiphytes.	Draw an image.

Describe phytoremediation.	Draw an image.

Describe aquaponics.	Draw an image.

Reading Science

Jenny's Plant

1. As Jenny sat by the apartment window, sadly looking out at the street, she finally understood what the expression *concrete jungle* meant. All she could see were concrete buildings, roads, and bridges for miles. A car horn blared angrily as if it shared Jenny's feelings about the city.

2. Jenny and her mom had recently moved from their farm in Iowa to an apartment building in the big city. After Jenny's parents split up, her mom could no longer afford to keep the farm. No amount of begging, pleading, and crying had made any difference in changing her mom's mind. Her mom's best friend lived in the city and got her mom a job in a nearby office building.

3. Jenny missed the farm. She missed the wide-open spaces and the trees, and mostly, she missed getting her fingers dirty with the soil. Planting and then watching the plants grow from seeds to seedlings, and, finally, to a mature plant that bloomed inspired her. She sighed as she looked around. There was nothing green that was living and growing in their small city apartment.

4. Just then, Jenny's mom came home from work, carrying a bag in her hand. "Wait until you see what I have for you!" she said excitedly.

5. "Is it a plane ticket back to our farm in Iowa?" Jenny asked with a scowl on her face.

6. "No, Jenny! You know that won't happen, but it is a little something that might remind you of it."

7. Jenny's mom opened the bag and pulled out a plant. She beamed as she presented it to Jenny. Jenny was confused. She did not know how she could care for a plant without a place to plant it. They did not have a yard or any place with soil. She turned her questioning eyes to her mom. As if she were reading her mind, her mom explained, "Plants do not always need soil to survive. This plant gets its nutrients from air and water."

8. Jenny's mom took out the instructions and showed them to Jenny.

Instructions for Your Air Plant

The nutrients hydrogen (H), oxygen (O), and carbon (C) are found in the air and water.

In a process called photosynthesis, plants use energy from the Sun to change carbon dioxide and water into starches and sugars. These starches and sugars are the plant's food.

Simply place your plant near a window, so it can receive enough light. Water your plant by submerging it in water at least once a week. Mist your plant between soakings.

9. After reading the instructions, she could not wait to get started! She found the perfect spot on the window ledge. It felt good to be caring for a living, growing plant again. "Thanks, Mom, for helping bring a little piece of the farm to the city."

# Reading Science

1. The author included the "Instructions for Your Air Plant" to help the reader–

   A. know why people purchase air plants.

   B. understand the process of photosynthesis.

   C. learn how to care for an air plant.

   D. Both B and C

2. Read this sentence from paragraph 1:

   All she could see were concrete buildings, roads, and bridges for miles.

   The imagery in these lines appeals most to the reader's sense of–

   A. sight.

   B. smell.

   C. taste.

   D. touch.

3. What can the reader conclude about Jenny's mom?

   A. She misses the farm as much as Jenny.

   B. She is frustrated with Jenny's attitude about the city.

   C. She wants to move back to Iowa.

   D. She wants to help make Jenny feel better.

4. The author includes paragraphs 1 and 2 to show that–

    A. Jenny's mom got a new job in the city.

    B. Jenny is unhappy living in the city and misses the farm.

    C. Jenny blames her mom for having to live in the city.

    D. there is a lot of concrete in the city.

5. What does Jenny's mom hope to accomplish by giving Jenny the plant?

    A. She wants to teach Jenny about photosynthesis.

    B. She wants Jenny to start a new hobby to take her mind off the farm.

    C. She wants to explain that there are different kinds of plants.

    D. She wants to make the new apartment feel more like home.

Name: _____ Date: _____

∞ **Open-Ended Response**

1. What do plants need in order to live and grow? Explain your answer.

_____

_____

_____

_____

_____

2. How is the way that plants get energy different from the way that animals get energy?

_____

_____

_____

_____

_____

3. Ana says that plants require mostly air and water to live and grow. Peter says that plants require mostly soil to live and grow. Who do you agree with? Why?

_____

_____

_____

_____

_____

Name: _____ Date: _____

 # Claim-Evidence-Reasoning

Scenario

You work for a plant nursery and need to figure out which resources plants need in order to grow larger. You observed several plants and tracked which resources they had access to and how much they grew. You recorded your observations for a month in the table below.

Plant	Access to Air	Access to Soil	Access to Water	Access to Fertilizer	Total Growth
A	No	Yes	Yes	Yes	0 cm
B	Yes	No	Yes	Yes	5 cm
C	Yes	Yes	No	Yes	0 cm
D	Yes	Yes	Yes	No	4 cm
E	Yes	No	Yes	No	4 cm

Prompt

Use scientific reasoning and the data from the table to make a claim about what resources a plant needs to grow.

Claim:

_____

_____

_____

_____

_____

Claim-Evidence-Reasoning

Evidence:

_____

_____

_____

_____

_____

Reasoning:

_____

_____

_____

_____

_____

_____

_____

_____

_____

Food Webs

Name: _____ Date: _____

 # Graphic Organizer

Food Chains

List examples of food chains in the squares below. Fill in information about plants, animals, and decomposers.

PLANTS

ANIMALS

DECOMPOSERS

Explore 1

Stringy Connections

1. Draw and label your class food web. Use arrows to show the flow of energy from one organism to another.

# Explore 1

2. Where does all energy originally come from?

_____

3. Which organism uses energy from the Sun to produce food?

_____

4. Name the following organisms that appear on your food web.

Producers

_____

Herbivores

_____

Carnivores

_____

Omnivores

_____

Detritivores and decomposers

_____

Name: _____ Date: _____

 **Explore 2**

Decomposition Race

Our Driving Question
What factors affect the decomposition process?

What We Need
1 Spray bottle with water (per class)

2 42 oz Disposable plastic containers with lids (per group)

1,000 mL Moist (not wet) garden soil (per group)

1 Newspaper sheet, cut into strips (per group)

2–3 Earthworms (per group)

1 Small apple, cut in half (per group)

Procedure
1. Put 500 mL of soil into each container.

2. Divide your paper strips in half and moisten with the spray bottle.

3. Put the moistened strips on top of the soil in each container.

4. Add one half of the apple to each container.

5. Place the earthworms in one of the plastic containers.

6. Make daily observations of the two containers for 2–3 weeks and record your observations in the data table on the next page.

Explore 2

	Week 1		Week 2		Week 3	
	Worms	No Worms	Worms	No Worms	Worms	No Worms
Monday						
Tuesday						
Wednesday						
Thursday						
Friday						

Reflection Questions:

Explain the differences you notice between the two containers.

_____

_____

_____

_____

_____

 **Explore 2**

What is happening to the apple?

_____

_____

_____

_____

When something decomposes, some of its matter goes back into the soil. How could this be a good thing for the environment?

_____

_____

_____

_____

How did the living organisms and nonliving matter interact with each other in this system?

_____

_____

_____

_____

What factors affect decomposition?

_____

_____

_____

_____

Name: _____ Date: _____

 **Explore 2**

Decomposition Race
Claim-Evidence-Reasoning

Prompt

Write a scientific explanation for what happened to the apple.

Claim:

_____

_____

Evidence:

_____

_____

Reasoning:

_____

_____

_____

_____

Name: _____ Date: _____

Linking Literacy
Post-Reading

Ocean Energy Description

Directions: Describe the transfer of energy you see in the Ocean Energy picture. Include the words *energy*, *producer*, *consumer*, and *decomposer* in your description.

_____

_____

_____

_____

_____

_____

_____

_____

_____

_____

_____

_____

_____

_____

_____

_____

_____

Reading Science

After the Fire

1. Two weeks ago, a fire destroyed much of the forest on the west bank of Silver Lake. It was started by a campfire that was not put out properly. Firefighters were able to control the blaze, but it still burned over much of the forest. Now, scientists are exploring the area to see how much damage was done.

2. Silver Lake was a popular destination for families to picnic, camp, and hike. In the **shallows** near the shore, long-legged birds such as herons and egrets could be seen by visitors. The waters were known to be great fishing grounds. And hikers often saw deer, rabbits, and armadillos.

3. But when Dr. Liz Jordan visited the lake yesterday, she saw a different scene. The area around the lake is now a black, charred landscape. The fire wiped out all the small bushes, ferns, and other undergrowth. There are still some blackened tree trunks that were stripped of their leaves and needles due to the fire.

4. When asked where all the animals and birds might be, Dr. Jordan was thoughtful.

5. "Well," she pondered, "animals are clever in the sense that they are often able to escape a fire. But the problem is that they won't be able to return here for quite some time."

6. Dr. Jordan explained that all the green plants play a special role in the ecosystem. "We call these plants *producers*. They use sunlight, water, and carbon dioxide to make their own food. Some organisms, however, called *consumers*, cannot make their own food. They have to consume, or use, the food from the plants to survive."

7. Dr. Jordan's assistant, Ben Scott, added, "All the animals in the forest depend on the producers, even the ones who do not eat plants. Rabbits, for example, are herbivores; they only eat plants. But a hawk is labeled a carnivore, because it only eats other animals. When the hawk eats the rabbit, it uses the energy that came from the plants that the rabbit ate."

8. "And that energy," said Dr. Jordan, "came from the Sun. It's a food web, with energy passing from the Sun to plants, to animals that eat plants, to animals that eat other animals."

9. A major fire, such as the one at Silver Lake, can destroy food webs, because it removes the producers from the chain. The consumers who survived the fire now have to find food somewhere else.

10. As Dr. Jordan and Mr. Scott started to leave the forest, however, Dr. Jordan stopped. She reached down and rooted in the ash for a moment, and we could see a small, green stem.

11. "Well," said Dr. Jordan, "it looks as though the producers are already on their way back."

Reading Science

1. The **shallows** of the lake (second paragraph) are probably–

   A. shorelines.

   B. water near shore that is not deep.

   C. deep water close to shore.

   D. water far from shore that is not deep.

2. Where does the energy in the food web begin?

   A. Fire

   B. Producers

   C. Consumers

   D. Sunlight

3. Fern is to producer as _____ is to consumer.

   A. tree

   B. sunlight

   C. rabbit

   D. water

4. What will probably happen next at Silver Lake?

    A.   Consumers will return, even though the producers have all disappeared.

    B.   Over time, producers will grow back, and when there are enough of them, consumers will return.

    C.   Producers will grow back, but consumers will have moved on and will never return to Silver Lake.

    D.   Another fire will destroy the east side of Silver Lake.

5. Another good title for this story would be–

    A.   "Where Have All the Producers Gone?"

    B.   "All about Dr. Jordan."

    C.   "Silver Lake Picnic Area."

    D.   "Put Out Campfires Properly."

Name: _____ Date: _____

 # Open-Ended Response

1. How are organisms in a food web dependent on each other?

_____

_____

_____

_____

2. Give an example of a food chain and describe the flow of energy through it.

_____

_____

_____

_____

_____

3. What are decomposers? How do they "recycle" matter?

_____

_____

_____

_____

Name: _____ Date: _____

Claim-Evidence-Reasoning

Food Webs

Scenario

Food webs model the relationships between organisms within an ecosystem. Every organism within a food web has a specific role. Some make their own food, some eat other organisms, and some, such as the dung beetle, eat the waste of other organisms.

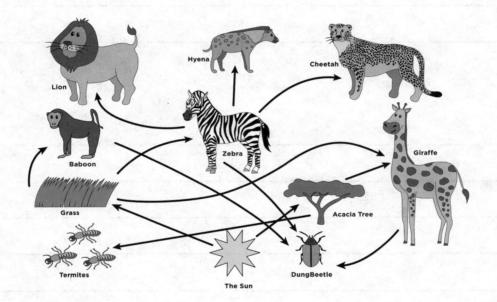

Prompt

Write a scientific explanation describing the relationship between the grass and the dung beetle.

Claim:

_____

_____

_____

_____

Claim-Evidence-Reasoning

Evidence:

_____

_____

_____

_____

_____

_____

Reasoning:

_____

_____

_____

_____

_____

_____

_____

_____

Ecosystems

Name: _____   Date: _____

Graphic Organizer

Animal Surroundings

Directions: Pick an animal and describe how its surroundings help meet its needs.

Describe the animal's ecosystem.

Describe how the environment meets its needs.

Animal:

Describe the animal's ecosystem.

Describe how the environment meets its needs.

Animal:

Describe the animal's ecosystem.

Describe how the environment meets its needs.

Animal:

What happens if a new species is added to the environment?

Name: _____ Date: _____

Explore 1

Zoo Tour

Procedure

1. Your group will get a zoo-animal picture card with general information about the animal.

2. Prepare a 2- to 3-minute presentation about your animal.

3. Create a 3-D model of a habitat that will meet the basic needs of your animal, and include the picture of the animal.

4. Use the space below to write out and sketch ideas.

My Animal:

_____

_____

_____

_____

Explore 1

Questions to Consider

1. How will your animal get water?

2. How will your animal get food?

3. What other basic needs does the habitat meet?

4. What are some living things that your animal depends on?

5. What are some nonliving things that your animal depends on?

6. How will your group present your habitat to the class?

7. Did your group meet all the criteria listed on the rubric?

Name: _____ Date: _____

Explore 2

What Do I Need?

Directions

Record the number of animals that did and did not survive after each round.

Round	Number of Animals That Survived	Number of Animals That Did Not Survive
1		
2		
3		
4		

How was each round different?

_____

_____

_____

What did a change in population cause?

_____

_____

_____

Explore 2

Why did the increase in population cause more animals to perish?

_____

_____

_____

_____

Name: _____   Date: _____

 **Explore 2**

What Do I Need?

Claim - Evidence - Reasoning

Prompt

Write a scientific explanation describing the relationship between population size and survival.

Claim:

_____

_____

_____

Evidence:

_____

_____

_____

Reasoning:

_____

_____

_____

_____

_____

Name: _____ Date: _____

Explore 3

The Burmese Python Challenge

The Problem

Scientists in the Florida Everglades have observed a great increase in the population of Burmese pythons. The Burmese pythons have no natural predators and can lay up to 36 eggs every spring. Their large population is beginning to upset the natural balance of the Everglades ecosystem. These pythons like to eat small birds and rodents, some of which are endangered in the Everglades ecosystem. If the python population continues to increase, it could mean extinction for some of the small, endangered birds. The local authorities are not convinced pythons are damaging the ecosystem and are currently not willing to adopt any plans to reduce the Burmese python population.

The Challenge

Create a blueprint of a device that will trap the invasive species of python but will not harm or kill the pythons, plants, or other animals in the ecosystem. Convince the local authorities to adopt your plan by creating a presentation to explain how Burmese pythons have damaged the Everglades ecosystem.

Criteria and Constraints

- The blueprint must be drawn with dimensions.

- The blueprint must be labeled and should include the type of materials used and why.

- The blueprint should include an explanation of how the design will trap a Burmese python without harming the python, plants, or other animals.

- The presentation of the design should be about a minute in length.

- The presentation of how pythons damage the Everglades ecosystem should be about five minutes in length and should include a description of the Everglades ecosystem before the introduction of Burmese pythons, how Burmese pythons came to live in the Everglades ecosystem, how the Burmese pythons affect the Everglades ecosystem, and how reducing the population will affect the Everglades ecosystem.

Explore 3

Brainstorm and Research

Write down any ideas about how you could master the challenge. If you need more information, write down what you need to know and gain permission from your teacher to research the answer.

Design Plan

Draw a blueprint of your device that will trap the invasive pythons. Remember to include an explanation of how the design will trap a python without hurting it or other plants or animals in the ecosystem.

Build and Test

Build your design and test it. Does it meet all the criteria and constraints? Use the space below to list what problems you need to fix in your design.

_____

_____

_____

_____

Explore 3

Refine and Redesign

How could you solve the problems you found during testing? Use the space below to draw your new design that should solve the problems.

Retest and Finalize

Build and test your new design. Does it meet all the criteria and constraints? If not, repeat the refine and redesign process. If it does, move on to planning your presentation.

Presentation Plan

Use the space below to plan how you will present your final product. Be sure to include who will speak and what you want to say. Your presentation should include the scientific ideas used to solve this design challenge.

Name: _____ Date: _____

Linking Literacy
Pre-Reading

Ecosystems Brainstorm

Directions: For each round, write the topic given by the teacher and list as many things as you can for that topic in the time allowed.

Topic: _____

Topic: _____

Topic: _____

Topic: _____

Linking Literacy
During-Reading

Ecosystems Frayer Model

Directions: Complete the charts below about living and nonliving things, using information from the text.

Definition and Characteristics	Picture

Nonliving Things

Examples	Nonexamples

Definition and Characteristics	Picture

Living Things

Examples	Nonexamples

Name: _____

Date: _____

Linking Literacy
Post-Reading

Claim and Evidence

Directions: After reading the text, provide four pieces of evidence that support the claim in the center box.

Evidence

Evidence

Claim

Living and nonliving things interact in an ecosystem.

Evidence

Evidence

Reading Science

Going on a Hike

1. Ben awoke to the sound of birds chirping loudly overhead. As he rubbed his eyes, he thought, "Well, if the birds are up, I guess I need to be, too." He slowly climbed out of his sleeping bag, enjoying the last little bit of sleep still lingering, and pulled open the flap of his tent. It was a beautiful morning, with the Sun already beginning to shine brightly. "This will be a perfect day for a hike," thought Ben. A section of the national forest had recently burned in an accidental fire caused by an unattended campfire, and Ben was interested in seeing how the fire had affected the area.

2. Ben ate a quick breakfast of scrambled eggs and bacon, then packed his backpack. He made sure he had plenty of water, his compass, and his walking stick. With excitement in his step, he headed for the trail.

3. Before long, he reached the part of the forest he was looking for. It was easy to recognize the signs of the recent forest fire. Ben noticed burn marks on the trunks of the trees, and many trees were **charred**. Luckily, though, most of the trees had survived the fire and had not burned to the ground. As Ben continued along the hiking trail, he noticed that the forest floor looked like a moonscape. The grass and leaves that usually blanketed the ground had all burned away, and he noticed that the forest seemed quiet. Although the birds were loud at his campsite, here the sky was empty and silent.

4. Ben began searching for the deer and rabbits that were common and easy to spot near his campsite, but he did not see any. "Hmm . . ." thought Ben. "No birds, rabbits, or deer. This forest seems deserted of animals." Just then, a park ranger turned the corner, almost bumping into Ben.

5. "How's your hike?" the ranger inquired.

6. "It's interesting," Ben replied. "But I was wondering why I'm not seeing any animals."

7. "That's a great question. It has to do with the recent forest fire."

8. The park ranger showed Ben an informational flyer and pointed to a diagram.

9. The park ranger explained that the forest was an ecosystem and the grass and leaves that had burned in the fire had been food for many animals. He described it like a spiderweb when one strand is broken, the web starts to unravel. What affects one part of an ecosystem affects the whole in some way. With the grass taken out of the web, the insects that feed off the grass leave, and if those insects leave, the animals that eat the insects have to leave to find food elsewhere, and so on.

10. While looking at the diagram, Ben replied, "Oh, that makes sense; but it's so sad."

11. "Oh, don't be too sad," the park ranger answered. "Mother Nature is pretty tough, and in a few short months, the grass will grow back."

12. "And when the grass comes back, so will the animals!" Now, Ben could not wait for his next visit to this part of the forest, and he knew Mother Nature would be busy until then.

# Reading Science

1. What words help the reader understand the meaning of the word **charred**?

    A. *Floor looked like a moonscape*

    B. *Burn marks on the trunks of the trees*

    C. *Forest seemed quiet*

    D. *Part of the forest*

2. The park ranger used the diagram to show Ben—

    A. all the animals that lived in that part of the forest.

    B. that the forest was a natural habitat to many species.

    C. that living things are connected and depend on each other.

    D. the different birds in the forest that preyed on snakes.

3. What can the reader conclude about Ben?

    A. He is disappointed in his hiking trip, due to the recent forest fire.

    B. He enjoys hiking and will probably return in a few months.

    C. He is concerned about the loss of animals and worries they will not return.

    D. He is new to hiking and is grateful for the ranger's help.

Reading Science

4. Which sentence best supports the idea that the grass was an important part of the ecosystem?

    A. *"Hmm . . ." thought Ben. "No birds, rabbits, or deer. This forest seems deserted of animals."*

    B. *"Mother Nature is pretty tough, and in a few short months, the grass will grow back."*

    C. *"And when the grass comes back, so will the animals!"*

    D. *The grass and leaves that usually blanketed the ground had all burned away, and he noticed that the forest seemed quiet.*

5. The author most likely compares the ecosystem to a spider's web because–

    A. spiders lived in that part of the forest.

    B. the burned grass was like a broken strand of a web.

    C. a hiker would expect to see a spider's web in the forest.

    D. spiders' webs are strong and are used to catch prey.

Name: _____ Date: _____

 # Open-Ended Response

1. Explain ways in which you meet your needs to survive and thrive.

_____
_____
_____
_____
_____

2. Explain why some organisms only live in particular environments.

_____
_____
_____
_____
_____

3. Zebra mussels that live in Lake Michigan are considered to be an invasive species. Zebra mussels compete with the native mussels for food, space, and oxygen, and are reproducing twice as fast as the native mussels. What do you think will happen to the ecosystem in Lake Michigan as a result?

_____
_____
_____
_____
_____

Name: _____ Date: _____

Claim-Evidence-Reasoning

Scenario

You have a tropical fish tank with live plants at your home. You won a goldfish at the local fair. You go home and put the goldfish into the fish tank. A few days later, the tropical fish start to die. The goldfish is thriving and eating often.

Week	Angelfish	Parrot Fish	Tetra Fish	Goldfish	Aquatic Plants
1	2	2	6	0	5
2	2	2	6	0	5
3	1	2	5	1	3
4	1	1	4	1	1

Prompt

Provide a scientific explanation describing what happened to the fish-tank ecosystem after the goldfish was introduced.

Claim:

_____

_____

_____

_____

_____

Claim-Evidence-Reasoning

Evidence:

_____

_____

_____

_____

_____

Reasoning:

_____

_____

_____

_____

_____

_____

_____

_____

Matter Cycles

Name: _____   Date: _____

Graphic Organizer

Cycle of Matter

Directions: Describe how matter can move through each stage of the cycle.

Plants

Animals

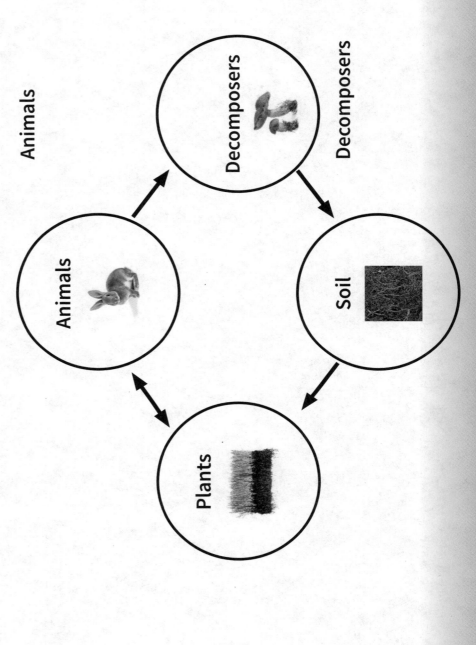

Decomposers

Soil

Name: _____ Date: _____

 **Explore 1**

Cycling of Matter

Use the space below to record your path as matter cycled through the environment.

Roll Number	What Happened?	Where Did You Go?
1		
2		
3		
4		
5		
6		
7		
8		
9		
10		
11		
12		
13		
14		
15		
16		
17		
18		
19		
20		

Explore 1

Use the space below to plan your group's matter cycle illustration.

Name: _____ Date: _____

 **Explore 2**

Composting

The Problem
Students in the recycling club have noticed the large amount of trash that is produced in the cafeteria each day. The students have asked the principal if they could start a compost heap to help reduce the amount of trash.

The Challenge
The principal said he would consider the idea, but the students need to present him with a plan and blueprint model.

Criteria and Constraints

- You must provide an outdoor location and scale drawing of the compost area.

- Your plan must include materials allowed in the compost heap, indoor collection, and responsibilities of the recycling club.

- You must address why composting is beneficial as well as its role in cycling matter within the environment.

- Your compost heap has a maximum size of 10 ft x 10 ft.

- Only members of the recycling club and school staff can be workers.

Explore 2

Brainstorm and Research

Write down any ideas you have about how you could master the challenge. If you need more information, write down what you need to know and gain permission from your teacher to research the answer.

Design Plan

Use the ideas you wrote down while brainstorming to develop a final design plan. Draw your plan and label the parts. Be sure to list what each part is made of.

Build and Test

Build your design and test it. Does it meet all the criteria and constraints? Use the space below to list what problems you need to fix in your design.

_____

_____

_____

Explore 2

Define and Redesign

How could you solve the problems you found during testing? Use the space below to draw your new design that should solve the problems.

Retest and Finalize

Build and test your new design. Does it meet all the criteria and constraints? If not, repeat the define and redesign process. If it does, move on to planning your presentation.

Presentation Plan

Use the space below to plan how you will present your final product. Be sure to include who will speak and what you want to say. Your presentation should include the scientific ideas used to solve this design challenge.

Name: _____ Date: _____

Linking Literacy
Pre- and Post-Reading

Matter Cycles K-W-L

Before you read: Think about different cycles. Record all you know about cycles in the first column of the chart below. In the second column, list what you want to know.

After you read: Look at what you wrote in the second column. Can you answer any of the questions you had? List all you learned in the third column of the chart below.

K What I Know	W What I Want to Know	L What I Learned

Name: _____ Date: _____

Linking Literacy
During-Reading

Cycle Models

Use the space below to draw a model of each cycle. Be sure to describe what is happening at each stage in the cycle.

Carbon Dioxide-and-Oxygen Cycle

Matter Cycles between Organisms and Their Environment

Name: _____ Date: _____

Reading Science

The Life Cycle of an Environmentally Friendly Onion

1. Everybody loves fresh, healthy vegetables, and everybody wants the environment to stay healthy. One way people can help the environment is to compost the food and living matter they don't eat or use. Just because a living organism dies does not mean that it cannot be put back into the cycle of matter.

2. Compost occurs when water, air, and bacteria break down material that has been alive. Material that has come from living organisms is called *biomass*. Compost piles at home often start out with unused food; yard material, such as dead leaves or grass clippings; and maybe some animal manure.

3. Let's say you have a hamburger for lunch one day. You like onions on your burger. You cut an onion, being careful to cut the top and bottom off, and peel back the tough outer layers of the onion skin. You can put the parts of the onion you do not use into a compost bin in the backyard. Other biomass is already "cooking." The bin can be plastic, wood, or just a pile in the yard. The fresh discarded onion attracts insects and worms. The onion also attracts tiny bacteria and other microorganisms that like to eat what you don't. You would not want to eat that onion now!

4. A compost pile needs plenty of material, air, and water. Then, the microorganisms can start to break down the material, producing heat and energy. This is where the phrase *cooking the compost* comes from. You will want to keep the pile moist. You must also stir it occasionally so that the material in the outer layers spends some time in the middle of the pile. Most of the decomposing action occurs in the middle of the pile. The more water, air, and biomass you put in the pile, the better your compost will get.

Reading Science

5. After a few weeks, the parts of the onion you didn't eat are a nice mushy goo. It has been broken down and released as energy by other living organisms. Your compost pile is now ready to be used in your garden. It is full of nutrients and mulch, which will help keep your garden vegetables stay healthy as they grow.

6. Your onion has taken an extraordinary journey around the cycle of matter. It began as a nice, round vegetable on the table. It changed from scraps in the compost bin to a pile of mushy, brown material, to wonderful nutrients for your garden. Never underestimate the power of an onion!

# Reading Science

1. Which of the following components is NOT necessary for successful composting?

   A. Air

   B. Moisture

   C. Plastic composting bins

   D. Bacteria

2. What is the main point of the reading passage?

   A. Oxygen is the most important component of a composting process.

   B. Compost can only be made of vegetables.

   C. Onions are the only vegetables that can be recycled.

   D. Living matter can live, die, and be broken down, producing a cycle of matter.

3. Which of the following statements is true about compost?

   A. Compost can only be made of vegetables.

   B. Compost starts with material bought at a garden center store.

   C. Compost starts at home, with unused food and yard material.

   D. Compost material is not good for a home garden.

 **Reading Science**

4. Which animals are essential for good composting?

    A. Spiders

    B. Insects and worms

    C. Dogs

    D. Cattle

5. What does the phrase *cooking the compost* mean?

    A. Letting the microbes decompose matter, releasing energy.

    B. Preparing vegetables for a meal.

    C. Spending energy preparing a compost bed.

    D. Burning papers to produce ash for the compost pile.

Name: _____ Date: _____

 # Open-Ended Response

Short Answer

1. Explain the cycle of matter as organisms take in materials from their environment and return materials to their environment.

_____

_____

_____

_____

_____

2. Describe how decomposers enrich soil and help other organisms survive. Be sure to describe what is produced during decomposition and how this benefits organisms in the environment.

_____

_____

_____

_____

_____

3. Describe the journey of an air particle as it moves from the air, to a producer, to a consumer, and back to the environment. Be creative and use additional paper as needed.

_____

_____

_____

_____

_____

Name: _____ Date: _____

Claim-Evidence-Reasoning

Scenario

Jayla and Shaun were hanging out at Nick's house as he was packing for vacation. Shaun asked Nick if someone was going to take care of his terrarium that was sitting by a window while he was out of town. Nick told Shaun that the terrarium would be fine without anyone around. He said he had not added anything to the terrarium or taken anything away. He showed Jayla and Shaun the chart he was using to track the population of each organism every month.

Month	Number of Worms	Number of Pill Bugs	Number of Plants
1	12	8	23
2	13	7	20
3	12	9	21

Prompt

Give a scientific explanation stating why Nick's terrarium did not need someone to care for it.

Claim-Evidence-Reasoning

Claim:

_____

_____

_____

Evidence:

_____

_____

_____

_____

_____

Reasoning:

_____

_____

_____

_____

_____

_____

Energy Transfer

Name: _____

Date: _____

Graphic Organizer

Energy in Living Things

Directions: How do living things gain energy? What do living things use energy to do?

PLANTS	ANIMALS

GAIN ENERGY

USE ENERGY

Name: _____ Date: _____

 **Hook**

Backtracking Energy

Draw a picture of your favorite food. Label the ingredients.

1. What plants or animals are used to prepare your favorite food?

_____

_____

_____

_____

_____

_____

Hook

2. Where do these ingredients come from?

_____

_____

_____

_____

_____

_____

Explore 1

How Plants Use Energy

Part I

Materials

2 Mint plants

1 Measuring cup

Water

1 Bucket

Procedure

1. Your teacher will place one mint plant in the sunlight and the other under a bucket.

2. Your teacher will water them equally every day for a week. Try not to let the covered plant get any light.

3. What will happen to a plant if we keep it in the dark for 1 week? Make a prediction. I think the plant we keep in the dark will _____ .

4. Observe the two plants every day for a week.

5. Draw and describe what each plant looked like each day on the data table below.

Day	Plant 1	Plant 2
1		
2		
3		
4		
5		

Explore 1

Was your prediction correct? _____

Would you rather eat a leaf from the plant that was in the light or from the plant that was in the dark? Why?

_____

_____

Where does the food energy inside a leaf come from?

_____

_____

Part II
Procedure

1. Observe each picture.
2. In the table below, explain how each plant is using energy.

Picture Number	Observation
1	This plant is using energy to _____ _____ .
2	This plant is using energy to _____ _____ .
3	This plant is using energy to _____ _____ .

Name: _____ Date: _____

 **Explore 1**

Energy and Plants
Claim-Evidence-Reasoning

Prompt

Write a scientific explanation about how the energy from the Sun is used as an energy source for plants.

Claim:

_____

_____

Evidence:

_____

_____

Reasoning:

_____

_____

_____

_____

_____

Name: _____ Date: _____

Explore 2

Got Energy?

Draw a diagram showing where plants, rabbits, and wolves get their energy. Use arrows to represent the movement of energy.

 **Explore 2**

What are some things that happened when you did not get enough energy in the game?

_____

_____

_____

_____

Where did all the energy originally come from?

_____

_____

_____

_____

Think about what the rabbits and wolves in the game had to do to stay alive. How do animals gain energy, and what do they use energy to do?

_____

_____

_____

_____

Name: _____ Date: _____

Linking Literacy
During-Reading

Describe with an Image

Directions: Answer each question in the first column. Then draw a picture in the second column to help explain your answer.

Where do all food chains and food webs get their energy?	Illustrate where all energy in a food chain or web begins.
How do plants make their own food?	Illustrate the process of plants using energy from the Sun to make their own food.
How do animals use energy?	Illustrate an action in which animals use energy.

Linking Literacy
Post-Reading

Write a Story

Directions: Imagine you are the Sun, shining down on the plants and animals on Earth. Write a story from the perspective of the Sun. Describe how plants and animals use your energy to survive. Draw a picture to illustrate your story.

_____

_____

_____

_____

_____

_____

_____

_____

Name: _____ Date: _____

Reading Science

Thanks to the Sun

1. Josh, hot and weary, trudged along the dusty road that led toward his house. He had been scouting hawks all afternoon, and now he was truly exhausted. To the right of the road was an endless field of corn, and sitting against the fence was Mr. Johnson, a local farmer. Mr. Johnson was in the shade of a sycamore tree, which looked rather refreshing. When the farmer waved to him, Josh happily trotted over and sat down, grateful for the chance to cool off.

2. "How do you stay out here all day in this blazing heat? I hate the Sun," Josh whined as he plopped down on the comfortable patch of grass next to Mr. Johnson.

3. "Well, then, let me acquaint you with the Sun," said Mr. Johnson. "What did you have for lunch today?"

4. "A hamburger and some fries—my favorite," said Josh, rubbing his stomach contentedly.

5. "Well, without the Sun, you certainly could not have enjoyed your hamburger or fries."

6. "What do you mean?" Josh asked with a quizzical expression.

7. While pointing toward the horizon, Mr. Johnson said, "See that field of corn plants over there? They need the Sun to grow so that they can produce ears of corn."

8. "Yes, but how does that relate to hamburgers?"

9. "Which animals around here consume corn?"

10. "Cows," answered Josh.

11. "Absolutely correct! And where do hamburgers come from?"

12. "Cows."

13. "Good. And where does a hamburger bun come from?"

14. While looking the farmer in the eye, Josh began to smile. "Wheat! And I know . . . wheat needs the Sun to grow and to make the wheat grains that are ground into flour. So, yes, corn, wheat, and cows need the Sun. And I guess I do, too, because I like hamburgers. But what about those delicious fries I devoured? Wait, I know. They come from those miraculous potato plants. They also need the Sun, right?"

15. "You have got it! We refer to all those plants as **producers**, because they produce, or make, their own food. They do not need to shop for food in grocery stores or grow food, like we do.

16. "I mean, it is pretty amazing, when you consider it," the farmer continued. "By using the Sun's energy, plants produce food through the process of photosynthesis. They transform the Sun's energy into food that they use to grow. We, on the other hand, are consumers. Consumers are living things that cannot make their own food. We have to get it from other sources, such as carrots, potatoes, onions, and eggplants. They are all producers that we can consume in order to obtain the Sun's energy; that energy allows us to walk, run, breathe, and even learn. The food items that are not picked might be plowed under, and decomposers return the nutrients to the soil. We call the transfer of energy from the Sun to the producers, to consumers, and, finally, to decomposers, a *food chain*."

17. As Josh nodded in agreement, Mr. Johnson stretched out his arms and smiled at the cornfield. "Well, you should probably meander on home now, so I can get back to my labors."

18. Josh stood up, thanked Mr. Johnson, and then sauntered down the road.

19. While humming a blissful song to himself, Josh looked up to the sky, squinted his eyes, and said a silent thanks to the Sun shining overhead. He did not feel so overheated now. In fact, he felt almost perfect. Still, Josh knew that he had to arrive home soon, so he accelerated his pace, kicking up dust as he went. Breathlessly, he opened the door, and he saw that he was just in time for a dinner of baked chicken, rolls, green beans, carrots, and milk—all things that began with the energy of the Sun.

20. "Hey, Mom! We are eating some producers, and I am going to consume all of them!"

 Reading Science

1. Which is the best summary of the story?

   A. A boy has a conversation with a farmer on a hot summer day.

   B. A farmer takes a break and talks to a boy.

   C. A boy learns about hamburgers.

   D. A boy discovers the importance of the Sun.

2. Which diagram shows an example of a food chain described in the passage (paragraph 16)?

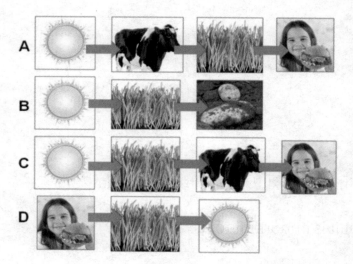

   A. A

   B. B

   C. C

   D. D

Reading Science

3. Which of these would be an example of a **producer**?

    A.   A chicken

    B.   A person

    C.   A carrot plant

    D.   A hamburger

4. Finish this analogy:
corn is to cow as French fry is to _____.

    A.   potato

    B.   Josh

    C.   tractor

    D.   cow

5. What will Josh probably think the next time it is a very hot day?

    A.   "The Sun is hot, but it is important to us."

    B.   "I hate the Sun!"

    C.   "I wish it would rain."

    D.   "I wish I had a glass of water."

Name: _____ Date: _____

Open-Ended Response

1. Why is the Sun's energy important for life on Earth?

_____

_____

_____

_____

2. How does the energy we get from food relate to the Sun?

_____

_____

_____

_____

_____

3. Why do plants need energy from the Sun? Why do animals need energy from food?

_____

_____

_____

_____

_____

_____

Name: _____ Date: _____

Claim-Evidence-Reasoning

Scenario

After studying living organisms in class, Destiny concluded that if all the plants in an ecosystem could not get sunlight for a long period of time, all the plants and animals in that area would die.

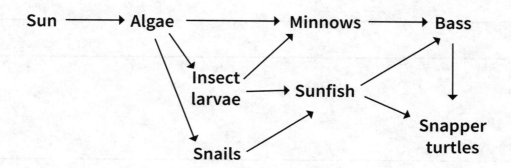

Prompt

Do you agree with Destiny? State your claim, provide evidence, and use scientific reasoning to prove you are correct.

Claim:

_____

_____

_____

_____

_____

_____

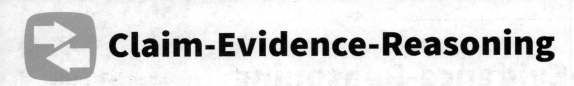

Claim-Evidence-Reasoning

Evidence:

_____

_____

_____

_____

_____

Reasoning:

_____

_____

_____

_____

_____

_____

_____

Earth's Systems Interactions

Name: _____

Date: _____

Graphic Organizer

Interactions on Earth

Complete each graphic. The top rectangle is the main sphere of the graphic. Record characteristics of that sphere in the rectangle. In the rectangles connected below, explain or provide an example of how those spheres interact.

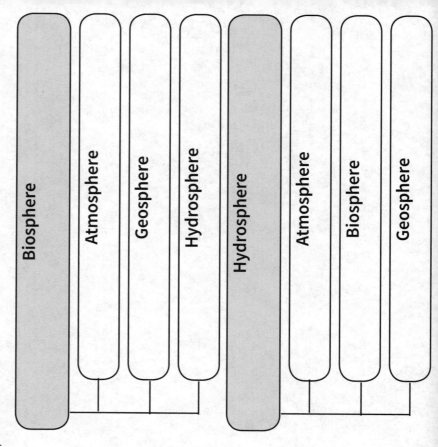

Biosphere

Atmosphere

Geosphere

Hydrosphere

Hydrosphere

Atmosphere

Biosphere

Geosphere

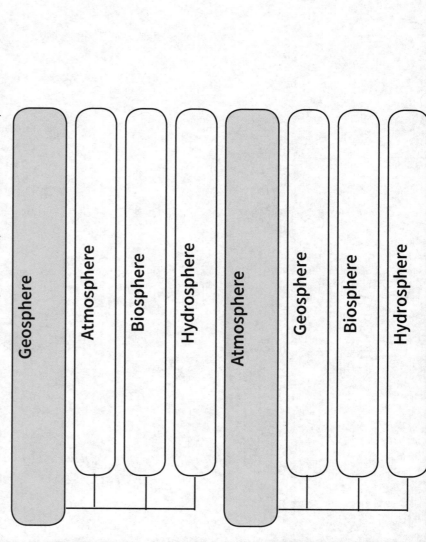

Geosphere

Atmosphere

Biosphere

Hydrosphere

Atmosphere

Geosphere

Biosphere

Hydrosphere

Earth's Systems Interactions

Name: _____ Date: _____

 **Explore 1**

The Four Spheres of Earth

Make a plan for your diorama.

 # Explore 1

What parts did you include in your diorama for each sphere?

_____

_____

_____

What is one thing you learned from the other groups' dioramas?

_____

_____

_____

_____

What could you do to make your diorama better?

_____

_____

_____

_____

Name: _____ Date: _____

 **Explore 2**

System Interactions

Station 1: Working Together

Use the space below to classify which organism would be best supported by each ocean environment. Briefly describe your reasoning behind which environment you chose for each organism.

Continental Shelf	Open Ocean

Use the information on the Ocean Organism Cards to identify and describe the relationship between the organism and the hydrosphere as well as between the organism and other members of the biosphere.

Seagrass	
Biosphere	Hydrosphere

Sea Turtle	
Biosphere	Hydrosphere

Explore 2

Herring	
Biosphere	Hydrosphere

Oysters	
Biosphere	Hydrosphere

Humpback Whale	
Biosphere	Hydrosphere

Describe how the hydrosphere and biosphere interact.

_____

_____

_____

Explore 2

Station 2: Cascade Mountains

Draw and label what happened to your model.

What happened to the water in the ocean?

_____

_____

What happened when the water vapor reached the mountains?

_____

_____

Think about all the ways Earth's systems were interacting in this model. Describe as many as you can in the space below.

_____

_____

_____

_____

_____

# Explore 2

Station 3

Draw and label a picture illustrating what happened as you dropped water on the sugar cube. Draw and label another picture showing what this could represent in real life.

Our Model	Real Life

What could the sugar cube and the water drops represent in real life?

_____

_____

_____

Which systems interacted here?

_____

_____

_____

Identify and describe the relationships between the systems.

_____

_____

_____

Name: _____ Date: _____

 **Explore 2**

Cascade Mountains
Claim-Evidence-Reasoning

Prompt

Using scientific reasoning, write a scientific explanation for how the geosphere (the mountains) affected the hydrosphere (precipitation) on the east and west sides of the Cascade Mountains.

Claim:

_____

_____

_____

Evidence:

_____

_____

_____

Reasoning:

_____

_____

_____

_____

_____

_____

Name: _____ Date: _____

 **Explore 3**

Modeling the Systems

Which two systems did you choose to model?

_____

Make a plan for your model.

Describe the components of your model and their interactions.

_____

_____

_____

_____

 **Explore 3**

Identify and describe the relationships between the systems you modeled.

_____

_____

_____

_____

How do the systems in your model work together to affect the Earth system?

_____

_____

_____

_____

_____

_____

How did one system in your model contribute to the functioning of the other system?

_____

_____

_____

_____

_____

_____

Name: _____ Date: _____

 **Linking Literacy**
Pre-Reading

Categorize It

Record how your class sorted the objects on the sticky notes. Use the examples you listed as a class to create your own description of each system below.

Biosphere	Hydrosphere
Examples:	Examples:
Description:	Description:
Atmosphere	**Geosphere**
Examples:	Examples:
Description:	Description:

Linking Literacy
During-Reading

Color Coded Notes

Directions: Use the note-taking guide to fill in the definition, description, and characteristics of Earth's systems.

| Define Geosphere: |
| Geosphere Characteristics: |

| Define Hydrosphere: |
| Hydrosphere Characteristics: |

| Define Biosphere: |
| Biosphere Characteristics: |

| Define Atmosphere: |
| Atmosphere Characteristics: |

Linking Literacy
Post-Reading

Earth's Systems Comic Strip

Use each box below to draw and describe one of Earth's systems. Be sure to include the hydrosphere, biosphere, geosphere, and atmosphere.

Reading Science

Earth Interacts

1. Frank and his class could not wait for their field trip to the Museum of Natural History. His class had been working all year to improve their science. Today would be the day when history would come alive; at least, that is what Mrs. Stevens had said.

2. After arriving, the class lined up to enter the museum hall. Luckily for Frank, the entrance to the museum was close to his favorite exhibit—dinosaurs! As soon as he walked in, a large wall with many colors caught his attention. It looked as though the wall was colored into different rock layers. Within those layers, Frank could see that there were fossils located throughout. Some fossils were of seashells, and others were even animal bones.

3. After getting closer to this wall, Frank noticed that the information card said that the planet was very old, or 4.6 billion years, to be exact. As the class continued to walk around, they saw that different Earth models contained different landforms. What looked like a mountain in North America millions of years ago was not the same as how it looked millions of years later. In other words, Earth's surface was always changing. "Hmm," thought Frank. "What would make the surface change?"

4. Frank did not have to wait long for his answers. He heard the soft sound of raindrops. Looking at the exhibit before him, he clearly saw how the part of the exhibit where the rain was falling had a small hole forming at the bottom. While he knew that the drops were man-made, he quickly realized that this also happened in nature. "Aha, it is weathering!" Just like that, he remembered the unit they had studied about how Earth's surface was always changing. He remembered that some of the changes were caused by fast events, such as volcanic eruptions, tornadoes, and earthquakes. However, what he was seeing before him was a model of an event that was slowly breaking down the rock and turning it into soil that could be carried away (eroded) by wind, water, or ice. This process could wash away fertile soil, but it was also responsible for creating new soil.

Reading Science

5. Frank could not believe that what he saw before him was the same thing he had learned about in class. He understood that both living and nonliving things were in the new soil. The new soil provided the food, building materials, and energy that people needed for survival. Without soil, nothing could grow. Without water to break down rock, new soil would not be made.

6. Little by little, Frank began to see how everything was **interconnected**. As he thought back, it all clicked! Without water or the water cycle, rocks could not be broken down, and plants would not be able to grow. Connecting all the steps, Frank asked himself, "What else is a part of this system?" The Sun! Without energy from the Sun, there would be no wind to weather rock and no climate or weather on Earth. Without climate or weather, there would be no water cycle. Without a water cycle, nothing would change, so nothing could live or exist!

7. Taken aback with awe at all this information, Frank felt astounded. He couldn't wait to see what other things he could learn today.

Reading Science

1. What is the main idea of this story?

    A. Fossils are important and can teach us many things about the past.

    B. Without the water cycle, there would be no life.

    C. Frank and his class went on a trip to the museum and explored.

    D. Frank discovered that processes on Earth, such as the water cycle and soil creation, are interconnected.

2. The author's purpose for writing this piece was to–

    A. persuade the reader to visit the Museum of Natural History.

    B. inform the reader about the water cycle.

    C. inform the reader about the interactions between Earth's systems.

    D. describe how rock layers were formed millions of years ago.

3. Here are some dictionary definitions of the word **interconnected**.

    1. To meet with another person

    2. To build items near one another

    3. Dealing with companies that supply equipment to customers

    4. To be or become related

Which definition is the best match for the use of the word **interconnected** in paragraph 6?

    A. Definition 1

    B. Definition 2

    C. Definition 3

    D. Definition 4

Reading Science

4. What evidence best shows that Frank understood Earth's systems interactions?

    A.   *Without water to break down rock, new soil would not be made.*

    B.   *He understood that both living and nonliving things were in the new soil.*

    C.   *Without energy from the Sun, there would be no wind to weather rock.*

    D.   *Taken aback with awe at all this information, Frank felt amazed.*

5. All the following lines are facts, EXCEPT–

    A.   *Some fossils were of seashells, and others were even animal bones.*

    B.   *Without climate or weather, there would be no water cycle.*

    C.   *Luckily for Frank, the entrance to the museum was close to his least favorite exhibit—dinosaurs!*

    D.   *Without energy from the Sun, there would be no wind to weather rock and no climate or weather on Earth.*

Name: _____ Date: _____

Open-Ended Response

1. How does the ocean influence climate?

_____

_____

_____

_____

2. Look at the picture and identify the Earth systems. How are the different systems interacting?

_____

_____

_____

_____

_____

3. Earth systems can interact quickly or over long periods of time. Give an example of how Earth can change quickly and an example of how it changes slowly. Describe how Earth's systems interact in these changes.

_____

_____

_____

_____

_____

_____

Claim-Evidence-Reasoning

Scenario

In 1980, the Mount St. Helens volcano in Washington State erupted! An eruption column of ash rose 80,000 feet into the atmosphere and spread to 11 different states. A mix of hot lava and pulverized rock raced toward Spirit Lake, which is miles away. Snow, ice, and several entire glaciers melted, causing massive mudslides that traveled 50 miles away. The mudslide buried 14 miles of the North Fork Toutle River with rocks, dirt, and trees. The blast was heard hundreds of miles away in parts of Montana, Idaho, and Northern California. However, it was not heard in areas much closer, such as Portland, Oregon, only 50 miles away. Hundreds of square miles of forest were reduced to wastelands, thousands of animals were killed, and 57 people were killed. Areas that received a very thin coat of ash actually showed an increase in crop production the following year. The crusting of ash helps retain soil moisture. In addition, the ash may provide beneficial chemical nutrients to the soil. Surprisingly, weather is also affected by a volcanic eruption. The ash particles that were thrown up into the air were good at attracting water droplets, causing a large Earth's Systems Interactionsamount of rain during the eruption. Some of the gases that were emitted during a volcanic eruption, such as sulfur dioxide, had an immediate cooling effect because they reflected sunlight away from Earth. Estimates of the damage and recovery costs of the Mount St. Helens eruption were near $1 billion.

Claim-Evidence-Reasoning

Prompt

Give a scientific explanation identifying how two of Earth's systems were interacting during the eruption.

Claim:

_____

_____

_____

Evidence:

_____

_____

_____

_____

Reasoning:

_____

_____

_____

_____

_____

California Instructional Segment
Mission Log

Mission Log

Anchoring Phenomena

How are Earth's systems affected by humans?

Mission Briefing

The Industrial Revolution, which started in the late 1700s, changed human lives through the use of machines for manufacturing things quickly. However, Earth suffered from this progress. You will be arguing for why a group of time travelers should be sent back to warn others about the negative effects and suggest solutions so the technological advances can still happen without damaging Earth.

- How can we represent systems as complicated as the entire planet?

- Where does my tap water come from and where does it go?

- How much water do we need to live and to irrigate plants?

- How much water do we have?

- What can we do to protect Earth's resources?

California Instructional Segment
Mission Log

Class Mission Log

Information Gained

Earth's Systems Interactions

Think back to what you learned before to do the following:

Create a flowchart showing how Earth's systems interact.

Water Sources

Where is most of the water on Earth found?

How much water is usable to humans?

Connection to Mission

Earth's Systems Interactions

Think back to what you learned before to answer the following question:

How would one system being polluted affect another?

Water Sources

Why is it important for us to protect our fresh water?

California Instructional Segment
Mission Log

Class Mission Log

Information Gained

Reducing Human Footprint

What effect do humans have on Earth?

What are some ways humans can reduce our human footprint?

Connection to Mission

Reducing Human Footprint

Think about how different events could negatively impact an environment. Complete the *Impact* column of the chart on the next page.

Think about how different events could negatively impact an environment. Complete the *Possible Solution* column of the chart on the next page.

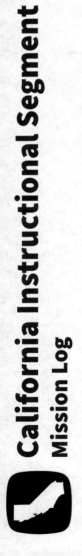

California Instructional Segment
Mission Log

Class Mission Log

Event	Impact	Possible Solution
Burned coal		
Waste materials buried		
Trash dumped in water		

Name: _____   Date: _____

California Instructional Segment
Action Plan

Action Plan

Create a presentation that encourages a time-travel company to send a group back to warn others about the negative effects of the Industrial Revolution and suggest solutions so the technological advances can still happen without damaging Earth.

Here's what we know about the impact of the Industrial Revolution:

- Coal burning caused air and water pollution.

- Natural resources were gathered quickly.

- Trash and other waste materials were usually dumped in waterways.

- Pollution caused illness and death.

- Acid rain did not exist until the Industrial Revolution.

- The invention of the assembly line meant goods were able to be produced much more quickly.

- We now understand the impact of pollution and have worked to clean up past damage and prevent future damage.

California Instructional Segment

Action Plan

Take Action

Design your presentation with your proposed solutions. Get creative! The best way to get people to listen is to keep them engaged!

Water Sources

Graphic Organizer

How Much Water?

Directions: Label the chart demonstrating the distribution of water on Earth. Create a symbol to represent each type of water source and add your symbols in the empty rectangles. Use the table at the bottom of the page to list examples of bodies of fresh water.

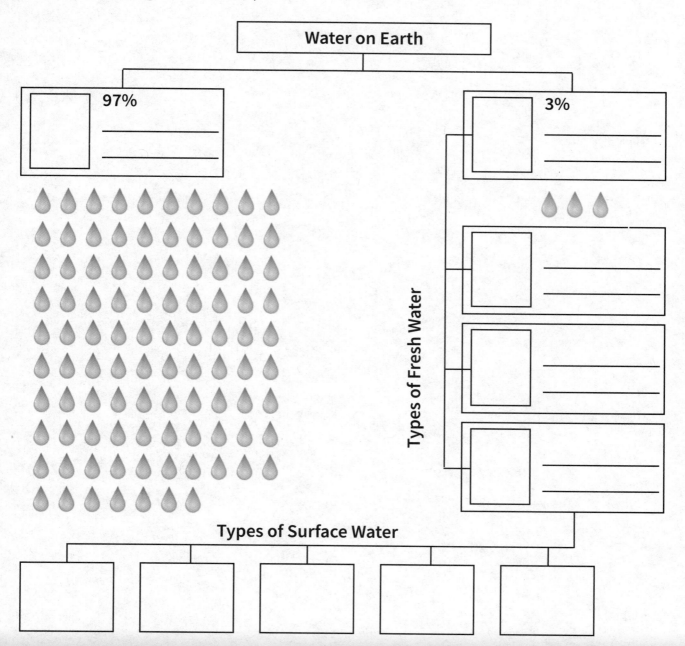

Name: _____ Date: _____

Explore 1

Where Is the Water?

Use the data from the index cards to create a bar graph that represents all the sources of Earth's water. Label the graph. Be sure to include the amount and percentage of water within each reservoir.

Title _____

What is the difference between salt water and fresh water?

_____

Where is the largest supply of water on Earth?

_____

Why do humans need fresh water?

_____

_____

Explore 1

Use the data from the index cards to create a bar graph that represents all the sources of Earth's water. Label the graph. Be sure to include the amount and percentage of water within each reservoir.

Title _____

Where is the largest supply of fresh water?

_____

_____

Are we able to use the fresh water that is frozen in the glaciers?

_____

_____

Which source of fresh water is easiest for us to access?

_____

_____

 **Explore 1**

Where Is the Water?
Claim-Evidence-Reasoning

Prompt

Jimmy volunteered to pick up litter from the local creek. He claims it is very important to protect streams and rivers from becoming polluted. Do you agree? Using scientific reasoning, write a scientific explanation that explains why you agree or disagree with Jimmy. Use data from the activity as your evidence.

Claim:

_____

_____

_____

Evidence:

_____

_____

_____

Reasoning:

_____

_____

_____

_____

_____

Name: _____ Date: _____

 **Explore 2**

Water Distribution Model Presentation

Sketch the design for your poster.

Explore 2

Create a script for your infomercial.

_____

_____

_____

_____

_____

_____

_____

_____

_____

_____

_____

_____

_____

_____

_____

_____

_____

Linking Literacy
During-Reading

Main Ideas and Details

While you read: Look for details in the text that give more information about the two text topics listed below. Record your main idea, examples, and two details for each topic.

Text Topic: **Fresh water**

Main Idea:	Examples:

Detail 1:	Detail 2:

Text Topic: **Salt water**

Main Idea:	Examples:

Detail 1:	Detail 2:

Name: _____ Date: _____

Water Sources

Linking Literacy
Post-Reading

Roundtable Review

After reading the text, read the questions below and write down your answers to the questions. Record why you think your answers are correct and cite evidence from the text. Discuss your answers with your group and record the group consensus in the final column.

Question	What Do You Think?	Why Do You Think That?	What Is Your Evidence?	Group Consensus
1. Does our Earth's large amount of salt water serve a purpose?				
2. How does the water cycle link fresh water and salt water?				
3. If we are able to treat fresh water for drinking, why do we need to conserve it?				

Reading Science

Under the Sea

1. I love the ocean, and I enjoy doing more than looking at it. I like to get under the surface and swim with all the amazing creatures that the ocean has to share.

2. To truly experience life underwater, I learned to scuba dive. *Scuba* stands for "self-contained underwater breathing apparatus." That is a fancy way of saying that when you scuba dive, you have a tank of your own air so that you can breathe underwater. Since I have learned how to scuba dive, I have seen some really amazing things.

3. For example, when I was in Hawaii, I went on a dive in the crater of a dormant volcano. The top of the volcano had been eroded by waves, so the entire thing was underwater. We **descended** into the crater to a depth of about 65 feet. We saw small octopuses floating through the water and sea cucumbers on the crater's floor. Sea cucumbers are not really vegetables! They are animals that look like cucumbers because they have dark, cylindrical bodies.

4. The highlight of that dive was the sight of my first shark. Before the dive, the guide had taught us a signal to use if we saw a shark. I thought he was just kidding, so I did not really pay attention. When I saw that shark, however, I was sorry I had not listened! I screamed into my regulator, which is the device that controls the flow of air from the tank. Luckily, sound travels very well in water, so my scream got everyone's attention. The guide swam up to the shark, waved his arms, hollered into his regulator, and chased the shark away. It turned out that it was a nurse shark. They tend to leave divers alone. Luckily, we were not really in danger.

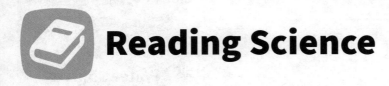

5. I have seen many awe-inspiring things underwater: manta rays, eels, and even a few more sharks. However, the ocean can be a dangerous place for humans who do not respect it. Still, I have always felt that the ocean was my friend. Scuba diving has led me to believe that we must take care of the ocean. Not only have I seen many beautiful things, but I have also seen the ways that we harm the ocean. For example, I have seen plastic bags and bottles floating in the ocean. Those are things that humans have thrown away, which are now polluting the water.

6. Why should we protect the ocean? Well, as I have seen, the ocean harbors many fascinating creatures. It is also important for our survival.

7. The ocean provides humans with the water we need to live. The ocean is the largest body of water on planet Earth. It covers about 71% of the planet. You might say, "How does it help us live?" Ocean water is salty. We need fresh water. When the Sun's energy heats the surface of the ocean and the water evaporates, the salt stays put in the ocean, while freshwater vapor rises. Later, that water vapor travels over land and becomes the precipitation we see. So, even though the ocean is salty, it still provides the fresh water that living things need to stay alive.

8. I have learned that the ocean is my friend. It takes care of me by providing me with water and by giving me a place to swim and dive. I want to be able to take care of the ocean by respecting it and telling people about how wonderful it is.

Reading Science

1. Which choice best summarizes the passage?

    A. Since I have learned how to scuba dive, I have seen some really amazing things. For example, when I was in Hawaii, I went on a dive in the crater of an extinct volcano.

    B. The ocean provides humans with the water we need to live. The ocean is the largest body of water on planet Earth.

    C. I like to get under the surface and swim with all the amazing creatures the ocean has to share. To truly experience life underwater, I learned to scuba dive. **Scuba** stands for "self-contained underwater breathing apparatus."

    D. I explored the ocean through scuba diving and learned that the ocean is my friend. The ocean takes care of me, and I want to take care of it by respecting it and telling people about how wonderful it is.

2. The word **descended** in paragraph 3 means–

    A. screamed.

    B. traveled downward.

    C. learned to scuba dive.

    D. swam in a crater.

3. Which of the following is the author's purpose?

    A. To teach the reader how to dive

    B. To inform the reader about the ocean

    C. To tell the author's personal experiences

    D. To teach the water cycle

4. What is likely the reason why the author screamed when she saw the shark?

    A.   The shark was swimming toward her.

    B.   The shark looked like it was going to bite the other divers.

    C.   Screaming was the signal her guide taught her.

    D.   She was happy to see a shark.

5. Which statement is NOT true about how the ocean water becomes the water humans use to survive?

    A.   The Sun causes the ocean water to evaporate.

    B.   Precipitation may have first been water in the ocean.

    C.   Salt cannot evaporate.

    D.   Heat slows evaporation.

Name: _____ Date: _____

 # Open-Ended Response

1. Why do the oceans play such a large part in the water cycle when they are only one of the many different bodies of water on Earth?

_____

_____

_____

_____

2. Water on Earth can be found in many sources. Where is freshwater located on Earth?

_____

_____

_____

_____

3. Most of Earth is covered in water, so why is it important to conserve water?

_____

_____

_____

_____

_____

Claim-Evidence-Reasoning

Scenario

The majority of Earth is covered in water. In fact, 97% of Earth's water is found in the oceans. Ocean salt water is unsafe for some plants, some animals, and human consumption. Fresh water comes from glaciers, lakes, streams, and our atmosphere.

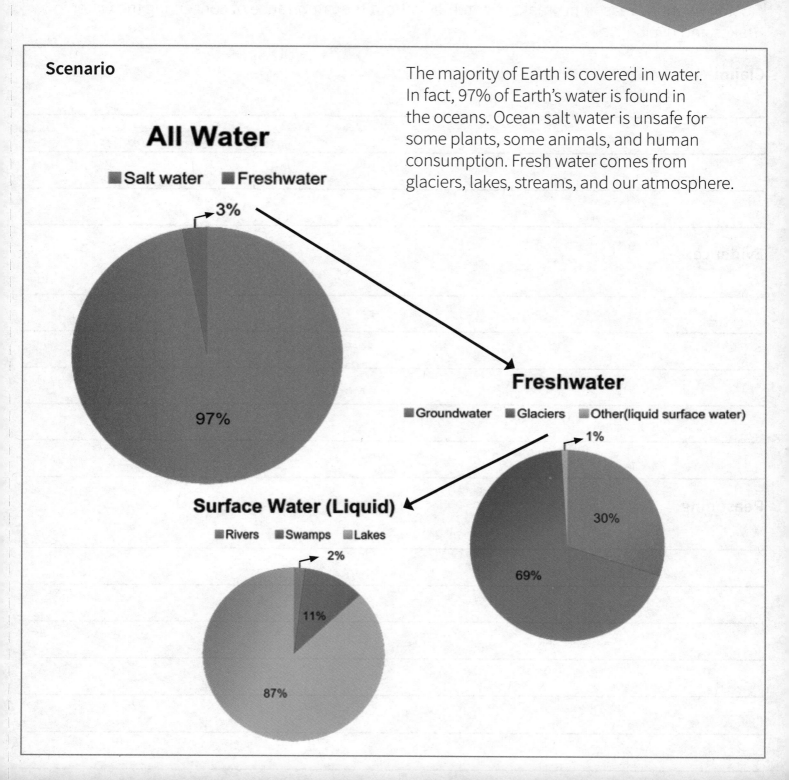

All Water

■ Salt water ■ Freshwater

3%

97%

Freshwater

■ Groundwater ■ Glaciers ■ Other(liquid surface water)

1%

30%

69%

Surface Water (Liquid)

■ Rivers ■ Swamps ■ Lakes

2%

11%

87%

Claim-Evidence-Reasoning

Prompt

Using scientific reasoning, make a statement about the importance of conserving the water in lakes and rivers.

Claim:

_____

_____

_____

_____

Evidence:

_____

_____

_____

_____

_____

Reasoning:

_____

_____

_____

_____

_____

_____

Reducing Human Footprint

Name: _____ Date: _____

Graphic Organizer

How Can You Reduce Your Human Footprint?

Explain a human footprint in each rectangle. In the arrow next to the rectangle, explain ways that the human footprint can be reduced.

Human Footprint

Ways to Reduce

Human Footprint

Ways to Reduce

Human Footprint

Ways to Reduce

Human Footprint

Ways to Reduce

Human Footprint

Ways to Reduce

Graphic Organizer

Human Footprint

Use the space below to record how the human activity affects land, vegetation, water, air, and outer space.

Effects on Land	**Effects on Vegetation**

Effects on Water	**Effects on Air**

Effects on Structures	**Additional Effects and Information**

Hook

Popcorn Resources

Use the table below to record your group's results. Then record the results of the other groups.

	Starting Amount Round 1	Ending Amount Round 1	Starting Amount Round 2	Ending Amount Round 2	Starting Amount Round 3	Ending Amount Round 3	Starting Amount Round 4	Ending Amount Round 4	Starting Amount Round 5	Ending Amount Round 5
Group 1										
Group 2										
Group 3										
Group 4										
Group 5										
Group 6										

Hook

1. Why did some groups end up with more popcorn than others?

_____

_____

_____

_____

2. Why did some groups run out of popcorn the first or second round?

_____

_____

_____

_____

3. What do you think the popcorn represents in the real world?

_____

_____

_____

_____

Name: _____ Date: _____

 **Explore 1**

The Fertilizer We Use

Draw and record your observations of the paper towel and water before the activity begins. Make sure to include labels.

_____

_____

_____

Draw and record your observations of the paper towel and the cup again. Include labels to show what has changed.

_____

_____

_____

 **Explore 1**

1. What happened to the groundwater?

_____

_____

_____

2. What happened to the paper towel (soil)?

_____

_____

_____

_____

Name: _____ Date: _____

 **Explore 1**

The Fertilizer We Use
Claim-Evidence-Reasoning

Prompt

Write a scientific explanation describing how farming can affect the environment.

Claim:

_____

_____

_____

Evidence:

_____

_____

_____

Reasoning:

_____

_____

_____

_____

 **Explore 2**

Acid Rain
Claim-Evidence-Reasoning

Prompt

Write a scientific explanation for the effects acid rain can have on a statue or building.

Claim:

_____

_____

_____

Evidence:

_____

_____

_____

Reasoning:

_____

_____

_____

_____

_____

Explore 3

Saving Earth

Introduction

Sara and Justin have just finished learning about humans' effects on Earth and are worried their community may not be informed enough! Every community has an impact on Earth that is both positive and negative. In these communities, people can either help protect and conserve the resources they use or pollute and trash them. Some communities are playing a part in helping save Earth's resources by cleaning up the pollution in their area and reducing their footprint on the environment. Sara and Justin have researched many different ways their community can help reduce their footprint. Follow Sara and Justin's lead by doing your own research on what your community and the communities around you are doing to help reduce their footprint. Is there more that can be done where you live? It's up to you to inform your community on what they are currently doing and how they can continue to help or make it even better!

What We Will Research

_____

_____

We need to look for answers to the following questions:

a.   Question 1

_____

b.   Question 2

_____

c.   Question 3

_____

Explore 3

Organize

Use this space to organize the information you gathered.

Record your sources below.

Source Used	Type of Source	Author	Is It Credible?

Explore 3

Present

Think about how you will present what you learned to the class. Use the table below to plan and organize what you learned to create your presentation.

How Will You Introduce Your Topic?	
Main Point 1 (What was the answer to your first question?)	
Main Point 2 (What was the answer to your second question?)	
Main Point 3 (What was the answer to your third question?)	
Summarize Your Main Points to End Your Presentation.	

Present your presentation to the class! Take some time to listen to feedback from your teacher and classmates. Discuss in your group what you did well and how you could have done better.

Explore 4

NASA Needs Our Help!

The Problem

Outer space is becoming a garbage dump. About 15,000 pieces of debris ranging from tiny paint flecks to 10-ton rocket stages are floating around space. Scientists warn that this may make future space ventures dangerous. How can we clean up the mess? Several methods have been proposed over the years. One proposed method is to collect the trash with some sort of device. Another proposed method is to get the trash to go toward the planet, where it will burn up in the atmosphere. Some ideas are cleverly low-tech; others seem like something from a science fiction movie.

The Challenge

Design a method of space-trash collection to clean up Earth's outer atmosphere. Create a blueprint of your method.

Criteria and Constraints

- The invention may only orbit Earth one time.

- There must be a reasonable form of destroying the trash collected.

- Your blueprint must be labeled and include measurements.

- Your group will have 20 minutes to research your idea before starting on the project.

Brainstorm and Research

Write down any ideas you have about how you could master the challenge. If you need more information, write down what you need to know, and gain permission from your teacher to research the answer.

Explore 4

Design
Draw a blueprint of your method for space-trash collection.

Build and Test
Build your design and test it. Does it meet all the criteria and constraints? Use the space below to list what problems you need to fix in your design.

Refine and Redesign
How could you solve the problems you found during testing? Use the space below to draw your new design that should solve the problems.

Explore 4

Retest and Finalize

Build and test your new design. Does it meet all the criteria and constraints? If not, repeat the refine and redesign process. If so, move on to planning your presentation.

Presentation Plan

Use the space below to plan how you will present your final product. Be sure to include who will speak and what you want to say. Your presentation should include the scientific ideas used to solve this design challenge.

Linking Literacy
During-Reading

Roundtable Discussion

Read the questions below and write down your answer to each question as you read about it in the text. Record why you think your answer is correct and cite evidence from the text. Discuss your answer with your group and record the group consensus in the final column.

Question	What Do You Think?	Why Do You Think That?	What Is Your Evidence?	Group Consensus
1. What can we do about littering?				
2. What can we do about water pollution?				
3. What can we do about air pollution?				

📖 Reading Science

Reduce, Reuse, Recycle

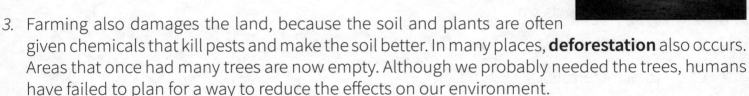

1. The seven billion people living on our planet need Earth's resources! Earth provides all the things that living plants and animals need. As the number of humans grows, so do the human footprints, or effects, on the environment.

2. Human footprints are not like those at the beach. These are footprints on the environment. Think about the energy we use. Energy does not just magically appear! It can come from sources such as fossil fuels, which must be dug up and made ready for human use. In the case of coal, it must be mined, which affects the land it's taken from and releases gases into the atmosphere when burned.

3. Farming also damages the land, because the soil and plants are often given chemicals that kill pests and make the soil better. In many places, **deforestation** also occurs. Areas that once had many trees are now empty. Although we probably needed the trees, humans have failed to plan for a way to reduce the effects on our environment.

4. One thing is for sure: before our human footprints become so bad that they can't be undone, we need to think about how we treat our planet. One way to do this is to guard what we have and think about the future.

5. The three Rs is a great way to start! If humans can reduce, reuse, and recycle, we can have a good impact on our Earth. We can reduce the number of resources we use by being less wasteful. One example would be to use less electricity. Also, instead of driving, we could walk or ride our bikes. We can also reuse items that we no longer use. We can give our older clothes, household items, and furniture to family or friends. We can even give them to charity. Recycling is another way that we can reduce our impact! When we recycle, we collect items, such as cans. When paper is recycled, it can be made into newer items, such as newer boxes. When plastic bags are recycled, they can be made into many items—even a carpet! Yes! Plastic trash bags can be made into carpet!

6. These small changes can have a big effect on our Earth! Although things cannot go back to being perfect, we can definitely make our planet better. Our atmosphere, soil, and land will be in a much better shape if we change the way we treat our planet!

Reading Science

1. Which choice best summarizes the passage?

   A. Recycling, reducing, and reusing are excellent for our environment. When you recycle, you can produce new items. These items include new boxes and even carpet!

   B. The number of humans on our planet is increasing rapidly. The more humans there are, the greater the use of Earth's resources!

   C. Deforestation takes place when many trees are cut down. Products can be made from these trees. Forests can provide wood for houses. Reusing paper helps protect trees.

   D. Earth's large population is using many resources. This has led to human footprints on our environment. When people reduce, reuse, and recycle, less damage occurs to our planet.

2. The word **deforestation** (paragraph 3) means–

   A. to use products smartly.

   B. to clear forests.

   C. to plant forests.

   D. to reuse tree products.

# Reading Science

3. Which of the following is the author's purpose?

    A. To educate the reader about how to recycle

    B. To persuade the reader to recycle

    C. To inform the reader about human footprints on Earth

    D. To inform the reader about fossil fuels

4. Why might the author have included the population count?

    A. The author wanted to present the substantial number of humans on our planet.

    B. The author wanted the reader to know how many products were made.

    C. The author wanted to introduce the opinion that humans have to recycle.

    D. The author wanted to show off the number.

5. Which statement is NOT true about human footprints?

    A. Once made, they can be reduced through careful planning and conservation.

    B. All humans depend on Earth's resources.

    C. Deforestation damages the environment.

    D. Deforestation is good for plants and animals.

Open-Ended Response

1. Describe one way that human activity can impact an ecosystem.

_____

_____

_____

_____

_____

2. Each year, billions of people use plastic grocery bags worldwide. Plastic is not biodegradable, and many times, the bags end up in our oceans. This plastic debris is greatly impacting our marine ecosystems. What could be a solution to this problem?

_____

_____

_____

_____

_____

3. Explain what people can do to reduce their damaging effects on Earth. Tell what you know about what is being done to protect Earth's resources and environments.

_____

_____

_____

_____

_____

Claim-Evidence-Reasoning

Scenario

Bradley and Jay were talking about where they want to go to college. Bradley said he wants to live in an environmentally friendly city, so Jay asked him how he would measure environmental friendliness. The chart below shows the information they found about the environmental performance of different cities. Each city was graded on the following qualities: mass transit (buses, trains, etc.), green space, alternative energy use, water conservation, and recycling. The higher the score, the more environmentally friendly the city is for that category.

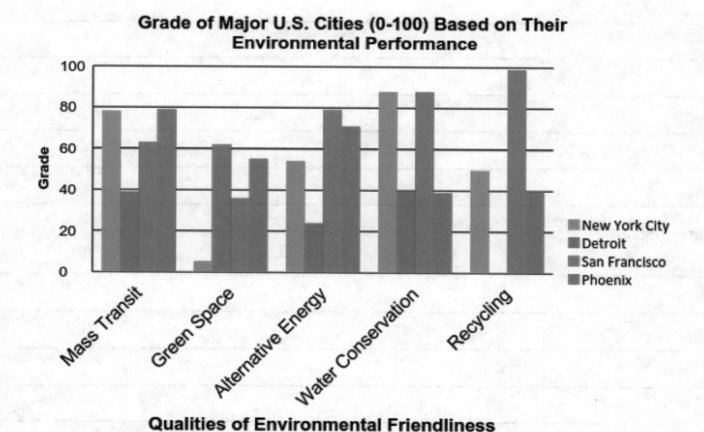

Claim-Evidence-Reasoning

Prompt

Based on the chart, which city should Bradley choose as the most environmentally friendly?
State your evidence and reasoning to support your claim.

Claim:

_____

_____

_____

Evidence:

_____

_____

_____

_____

_____

Reasoning:

_____

_____

_____

_____

_____

_____

Name: _____   Date: _____

California Instructional Segment
Mission Log

Mission Log

Anchoring Phenomena

Can we use patterns on Earth to help us solve problems?

Mission Briefing

You are the producer of a new show called *Surviving the Wild*. You need to make a survival guide to help the contestants on your show. Use the information you gather through your mission to create the guide and help them survive in the wild!

- What is our closest star?
- Can we use patterns in the movement of the stars to tell us anything?
- Do shadows caused by the Sun move in the same direction?
- In what direction does the force of gravity pull?

California Instructional Segment
Mission Log

Class Mission Log

Information Gained

Gravity

What is the direction of Earth's gravitational pull?

How could we lessen the effects of Earth's gravitational pull on an object falling toward Earth?

Earth's Rotation

What trends and patterns are there in the apparent movement of the Sun?

Connection to Mission

Gravity

What are two ways you can use gravity to help you in the wild?

Earth's Rotation

How can you use shadow patterns to help you survive?

California Instructional Segment

Mission Log

Class Mission Log

Information Gained

Observing the Stars

Which star is the closest to us? How do you know?

Objects in the Sky

Why do we see phases of the Moon?

Connection to Mission

Observing the Stars

What are some ways the Sun is helpful to you?

What are some ways the Sun is harmful to you?

Brainstorm some ideas for how to protect yourself from being harmed by the Sun in the wild.

Objects in the Sky

How could the Moon be helpful for surviving?

How can constellations be helpful if you are surviving in the wild with no technology?

Name: _____ Date: _____

California Instructional Segment
Action Plan

Action Plan

Create a survival guide for the contestants on your show to help them survive in the wild!

Here's what we know:

- There are predictable patterns in the sky.

- The Sun rises in the east and sets in the west.

- We see different moon phases every night.

- The Moon orbits Earth near the equator.

- Gravity is a force that pulls things down.

- The Sun is the closest star to Earth.

California Instructional Segment

Action Plan

Take Action

To survive in the wild, you must gather food and water, track time, find shelter, and keep yourself safe. Describe how you could use gravity and patterns in the day and night sky to help you meet all these needs.

Food	Water
Shelter and Safety	**Tracking Time**

![California Instructional Segment logo]

California Instructional Segment

Action Plan

Take Action

Use the space below to create your survival guide. Cut along the solid line and fold along the dotted line.

Gravity

 **Graphic Organizer**

Gravity

Directions: Draw arrows to show the direction the objects listed around the sphere are pulled because of gravity. List facts about gravity inside the sphere representing Earth.

Airplane

Human

Gravity

_____

_____

_____

_____

_____

_____

_____

_____

_____

Plant

Basketball

Explore 1

Earth's Forces

Our Driving Question
What is the effect of the pull of gravity on objects on Earth?

Materials
1 Strong magnet (per group)

1 Ruler, metric (per group)

1 Paper clip (per group)

1 8-inch piece of string (per group)

Procedure
1. Tie the paper clip to one end of the string.

2. Hold the magnet under the paper clip on the string.

3. Take turns holding the magnet in one hand and the paper clip on a string in the other hand. Move the string all around the top, bottom, and sides of the magnet so that the paper clip is affected by the magnet without touching it.

4. Look at the globe and think about people who live on the side or near the bottom of Earth. Use the paper clip and magnet to model how gravity affects people who live in those places. Discuss with your group why these people do not fall off the side or bottom of Earth. Record your ideas on the next page.

5. Put the ruler on a flat, smooth surface. Tape the ruler to the surface so that it does not move.

6. Tape the magnet in the center of the ruler at 15 cm.

7. Hold the string with the paper clip directly over the magnet. Does the magnet pull the paper clip toward it?

8. Record your results in the correct answer column on the next page.

9. Move the paper clip to the 14 cm mark on the ruler and repeat. Record your results. Continue to repeat the process at each centimeter mark until you reach the 0 cm mark.

10. After recording the results for 15 cm to 0 cm, hold the string with the paper clip over the 16 cm mark.

11. Record your results in the correct answer column on the next page.

12. Continue to repeat the process at each centimeter mark until you reach the 30 cm mark.

13. Analyze the data on the chart and answer the questions on the final page.

Use the space below to draw and describe how the paper clip interacted with the magnet as you moved the string around the magnet.

Explore 1

Record all data from your investigation in the table below.

Distance	Does the Paper Clip Move to the Magnet?	Distance	Does the Paper Clip Move to the Magnet?
15 cm			
14 cm		16 cm	
13 cm		17 cm	
12 cm		18 cm	
11 cm		19 cm	
10 cm		20 cm	
9 cm		21 cm	
8 cm		22 cm	
7 cm		23 cm	
6 cm		24 cm	
5 cm		25 cm	
4 cm		26 cm	
3 cm		27 cm	
2 cm		28 cm	
1 cm		29 cm	
0 cm		30 cm	

Moving farther away

Explore 1

Reflection

1. How is this model similar to and different from what happens in the real world?

Similar:

_____

_____

_____

Different:

_____

_____

_____

2. What did you notice as the paper clip was moved farther away from the magnet?

_____

_____

_____

_____

3. What does this tell you about Earth's gravity?

_____

_____

_____

_____

Explore 1

Earth's Forces

Claim-Evidence-Reasoning

Prompt:

Using a scientific explanation, describe how Earth's gravity affects objects

Claim:

_____

_____

_____

_____

Evidence:

_____

_____

_____

_____

Reasoning:

_____

_____

_____

_____

_____

Linking Literacy
Pre-Reading

Preview and Predict

Directions: Follow the instructions and answer the questions in the table below before reading the text.

Preview	Predict
What is the title of this STEMscopedia?	What do you already know about this topic?
Look at the pictures and their captions. Draw one of the pictures that seems the most interesting to you.	List two things you think you will be learning more about, based on the pictures and captions. 1. 2.
Read the first sentence of each paragraph on pages 1–3. Copy the sentences in the space below:	Based on what you just read, write two questions that you hope to answer by reading the text. 1. 2.

Name: _____ Date: _____

Linking Literacy
During-Reading

Outline Notes

Directions: Fill in the missing pieces of the notes while you read the text. Add in your own notes as needed.

1. Gravity is the force that pulls or attracts.

   a.   Gravity is always a _____ and never a _____ .

   b.   Gravity is a force of attraction between_____ or more objects.

   c.   We notice Earth's gravity because it is so_____ .

2. Sir Isaac Newton

   a.   Sir Isaac Newton started thinking about forces in the universe after

   _____ .

3. Gravity holds the solar system together.

   a.   The _____is the most massive object in our solar system.

   b.   Therefore, _____ .

   c.   The Sun's gravity causes other objects in the solar system, such as

   _____ , _____ , and _____ ,

   to orbit, or move around, the Sun.

   d.   These objects have their own_____ pulls,

   but they revolve around the Sun because the Sun is much more

   _____ .

Linking Literacy
During-Reading

Use the space below to add any additional notes or interesting facts.

_____

_____

_____

_____

_____

_____

_____

_____

_____

_____

_____

_____

_____

_____

_____

_____

_____

Linking Literacy
Post-Reading

Walk Around Paragraph

Write a sentence to answer the question below. At your teacher's signal, move to another student's paper, read his or her sentence, and write another sentence that expands on his or her thought. You will continue this pattern until you and your classmates have written an entire paragraph.

How does gravity affect other objects?

In addition . . .

Also . . .

Finally . .

Reading Science

Gravity

1. Jessica had compiled a list of the top-20 activities she hoped to accomplish this year. She double-checked her list, and there it was, number 14: ride a roller coaster. It was already November, so she needed to get serious if she wanted to complete her list on time. She convinced her family to head to the amusement park for their weekend destination.

2. "I'm the oldest, so I say we sit in the first cart," Jessica declared. She was only 11, but she was still older than her two brothers, Mike, who was 9, and Johnny, who was 7. "Besides, it's my list!" The family was impatiently waiting in line for their turn to ride the roller coaster. The roller coaster was famous for its 150-foot elevation and drop, and all the kids were excited to experience it. The coaster reached speeds of 65 mph. However, the problem was that they all thought that different carts would be the best spot to sit in to experience the speed. Jessica wanted the first cart, Mike wanted the last cart, and Johnny wanted the middle cart.

3. "No!" Johnny argued. "I'm telling you, the middle cart would be great!"

4. "No way! I want to sit in the first cart, so we can see what's coming up!" Jessica insisted. "I don't want my vision blocked by people in front of me."

5. "Guys, we all know the last one would be the most fun! Right, Dad?" Mike asked. "It would be the best for the big drop, right?" Their dad turned and faced all the kids.

6. "Actually, if you want to get the most out of the drop, then Mike is right. The rear cart is the best spot on a roller coaster, because the twists and turns are more noticeable," their dad said. Jessica and Johnny scowled as they looked down toward the ground. Mike grinned and said, "I told you so!"

7. "It all depends on the force of gravity, so the last cart would be the best," their dad explained. "When the carts start traveling up the hill, it slows down, because gravity is pulling on it from behind; but when the first cart makes it over the **apex**, gravity pulls the cart down the other side of the hill. So, because of the pull of gravity, the first cart starts to accelerate, which accelerates the second cart, then the third cart, and so on, like a chain reaction."

8. "So, by the time the last cart finally arrives at the top, it'll be speeding like a rocket!" Mike proudly exclaimed.

9. Jessica and Johnny were both angry that Mike was right, but they still agreed to the last cart. After all, Jessica did want to cross number 14 off her list! The family waited anxiously as the line got shorter and shorter.

10. "Which cart?" the man who was in charge of the roller coaster asked.

11. Mike smiled and proudly replied, "We want the last one. Since the force of gravity will start to pull on the first cart at the beginning of the drop, the last cart will receive the most acceleration!"

12. "Well, kid, it looks like you know your stuff. The last one it is!" The man stepped aside as they piled into the last cart. The kids had butterflies in their stomachs as the roller coaster jerked forward and they slowly ascended. They gripped the handlebars as they got nearer and nearer to the top. The first cart lurched over the tip, and everyone screamed. Jessica and her family raised their arms in the air as, one by one, the carts were hauled over by the carts in front of them, and soon the last cart went racing over the top!

13. All too soon, the coaster's acceleration decreased, and the ride slowly came to a stop. Jessica hated to admit it, but Mike had made her number-14 activity awesome!

Reading Science

1. The author uses figurative language in paragraph 8 to emphasize–

   A.   how the roller coaster looks.

   B.   that the roller coaster is very loud.

   C.   the roller coaster's speed.

   D.   the roller coaster's up-and-down movement.

2. Which of the following details supports the conclusion that Jessica likes to be right?

   A.   *"Besides, it's my list!"*

   B.   *Jessica hated to admit it, but Mike had made her number-14 activity awesome!*

   C.   *"I'm telling you, the middle cart would be great!"*

   D.   *Jessica wanted the first cart, Mike wanted the last cart, and Johnny wanted the middle cart.*

3. Paragraphs 2 through 5 are important, because they show–

   A.   the setting of the story.

   B.   the ages of the kids.

   C.   how tall and fast the roller coaster is.

   D.   the problem in the story.

Reading Science

4. Which words help the reader know the meaning of the word **apex**?

    A.   *Arrives at the top*

    B.   *Starts to accelerate*

    C.   *Pulls the cart down*

    D.   *Like a chain reaction*

5. Which sentence best supports the idea that gravity plays a part in the speed of the roller coaster carts?

    A.   *"Well, kid, it looks like you know your stuff. The last one it is!"*

    B.   *"The rear cart is the best spot on a roller coaster, because the twists and turns are more noticeable."*

    C.   *"Because of the pull of gravity, the first cart starts to accelerate, which accelerates the second cart, then the third cart, and so on."*

    D.   *Jessica and her family raised their arms in the air as, one by one, the carts were hauled over by the carts in front of them, and soon the last cart went racing over the top!*

6. Which is the best summary of this story?

A. Jessica had a list of 20 activities she wanted to accomplish. She had already done 13 of them, and she wanted to complete the next one. She convinced her family to go to the amusement park for the weekend. There, they rode the roller coaster, and Jessica was able to cross number 14 off her list.

B. Jessica and her family were about to ride a roller coaster, which was number 14 on Jessica's list of activities to accomplish. Jessica and her brothers disagreed on which cart would be the best to sit in for the ride. Jessica's dad explained how gravity made the last cart the fastest, so they all decided to sit there. At the end of the ride, Jessica was glad they had chosen the last cart.

C. Jessica and her family went to an amusement park. They all decided to ride the roller coaster, but everyone argued about where to sit. Jessica became angry, because she was the oldest and felt like her brothers should listen to where she wanted to sit. Finally, her dad made the decision, and they all sat in the last cart.

D. Jessica and her family went to the amusement park to ride the famous roller coaster. The roller coaster had a 150-foot elevation and drop, and the kids could not wait to ride it. The coaster reached speeds of 65 mph. However, the kids argued about where the best spot to sit was to experience the speed. Jessica wanted the first cart, Mike wanted the last cart, and Johnny wanted the middle cart.

Name: _____ Date: _____

∞ Open-Ended Response

Short Answer

1. How can you prove that we are affected by the pull of gravity?

_____

_____

_____

2. Choose one of your favorite hobbies or sports. Write about how this activity is affected by gravity.

_____

_____

_____

_____

3. Describe a day in your classroom without gravity. What would the objects around the room do without gravity? How would things be different?

_____

_____

_____

_____

Claim-Evidence-Reasoning

Gravity

Scenario

Stephen waited anxiously as he moved closer and closer to the front of the line for the new ride, Monster. He had been excitedly waiting for the opening of the new ride for months! Nothing was going to stop him from riding this coaster! Stephen was so mesmerized by the coaster that he hardly noticed the beads of sweat running down his forehead. It was finally his turn! He strapped in tightly and squealed in anticipation, clutching his park map in his right hand. He heard the ride manager start to count down. BOOM! The ride took off, working hard to pull Stephen high up the track incline before letting the coaster go down. Each time the coaster reached a peak, Stephen's stomach dropped as he was rapidly pulled back toward Earth. What a rush! Suddenly, his map slipped from his hands. Stephen watched as it quickly fell to the ground, but his worry didn't last long. He was soon screaming with joy as the ride took him on another terrifying drop! Stephen knew the ride had been well worth the wait.

Claim-Evidence-Reasoning

Prompt
Write a scientific explanation about the direction of Earth's gravitational force, using the evidence in the scenario.

Claim:

_____

_____

_____

_____

Evidence:

_____

_____

_____

_____

_____

_____

Reasoning:

_____

_____

_____

_____

_____

_____

Earth's Rotation

Name: _____

Date: _____

Graphic Organizer

Earth's Rotation

Directions: Draw a diagram to illustrate the cause of each pattern. Be sure to label and explain.

Night and Day	Changes in Length and Direction of Shadows

Name: _____ Date: _____

 # Explore 1

Shadow Tracker

Our Driving Question
How do shadows change throughout the day?

What We Need
1 Pencil

1 Piece of tape or sidewalk chalk to mark position

1 Ruler

1 Compass

1 Computer, if creating a digital graph

1 Paper plate

1 Quarter-sized ball of modeling clay

1 Straw

Procedure
1. Flip your paper plate over to its convex side.

2. Locate the center of the paper plate by folding it in half in both directions and marking a dot with your pencil where the folds intersect in the middle.

3. Anchor the drinking straw, using a small ball of clay, to the center of the plate where you marked the dot.

4. Label your sundial with the cardinal directions (N, S, W, and E) at the end of the folds.

5. Take your preconstructed sundial outside in a sunny area of the playground or parking lot and lay it on a flat surface.

6. Using a compass, find the north direction and align the north point of the sundial with it.

7. Be sure to mark the position of the sundial with a 2 cm piece of tape or sidewalk chalk to ensure that the sundial is in the same position every time. It should not be moved during the investigation.

8. Trace the shadow cast by the straw onto the paper plate throughout the day and label each tracing with the time. Pay close attention to the length and position of the shadow that is cast as well as the location of the Sun.

9. Measure the length of the shadow using a ruler, then record the measurements and observations in the data table below.

10. Using the data recorded below, create a bar graph to show the length of each shadow and the time of day. You may draw the graph on the next page or use a computer to create a digital graph.

Use the table below to record your data and observations.

Time of Shadow	Length of Shadow (cm)	Direction of Shadow

Explore 1

1. What did you notice about the shadow as time progressed?

_____

_____

_____

2. What did you notice about the Sun's movement across the sky?

_____

_____

_____

3. Did the Sun really move across the sky? _____ Why did it appear to move across the sky?

_____

_____

_____

_____

1. Using the data you collected on the chart, make a bar graph showing the length of each shadow (in cm) for each hour.

2. Make sure you label your axes and give your graph a title.

Shadow Tracker

Explore 1

Shadow Tracker

Claim-Evidence-Reasoning

Prompt

Think about the lengths of the shadows, and write a scientific explanation about when a shadow is the shortest.

Claim:

_____

_____

_____

_____

Evidence:

_____

_____

_____

_____

Reasoning:

_____

_____

_____

_____

_____

Explore 2

Hours of Daylight

Background

Earth's rotation on its axis causes day and night. Not only does Earth rotate on its axis, but as it rotates, it orbits the Sun. Earth is tilted on its axis as it orbits. This tilt causes the amount of direct sunlight that hits the Northern and Southern Hemispheres to change throughout the year. Scientists at the United States Naval Academy gathered data on the hours of daylight in Washington, DC, for 50 different days. This data set contains information for each season.

Question to Ponder

Is there the same amount of daylight each season of the year?

Procedure

Go to the data set on hours of daylight. Under **Attributes** on the left-hand side of the screen, click on **Hours of daylight in decimals in Washington, DC.** Drag it to the y-axis where it says, **Drag and drop here**. Drop it there. Then go to **Attributes** and click on **Seasons.** Drag it to the x-axis where it says, **Drag and drop here.** Drop it there. Hover your cursor over **Bar** at the top and click on **Bar chart.** On the left-hand side of the screen, click on **Time.** This will shade the bars in your chart by the time of year. The lightest color is the beginning of the year and the darkest color is the end of the year. You have created a bar chart showing the number of daylight hours in Washington, DC, during each different season. Use your cursor to hover over each bar to see the number of daylight hours for that day.

1. What is the least number of daylight hours listed on the y-axis?

   _____

2. What is the greatest number of daylight hours listed on the y-axis?

   _____

3. The length of 1 day is 24 hours. Why isn't the most amount of daylight 24 hours?

   _____

4. What information is given on the x-axis?

   _____

5. What does each bar represent?

   _____

Explore 2

Look at the information given in the boxes at the top of the data set. Click on **Stats.** Then slide down and click on **Mean.** This adds a red line to the data set that gives the mean (average) amount of daylight for each season in Washington, DC. Use your cursor to hover over the red line to view the mean for each season. Using information from the data set, fill in the chart below.

	Fall	Winter	Spring	Summer
Mean Hours of Daylight				
Longest Day				
Shortest Day				

1. On the chart, circle the amount of daylight on the shortest day of the year. In which season is this day? _____

2. On the chart, put a box around the amount of daylight on the longest day of the year. Which season is this day?_____

3. Which season has the most mean hours of daylight? The shortest?

   _____

4. Which season has a pattern of longer days? Shorter days?

   _____

5. Describe any patterns you notice in the length of daylight in the fall and spring.

   _____

   _____

   _____

6. Using the information on the data set and the chart, describe how the amount of daylight changes throughout the year.

   _____

   _____

   _____

   _____

Name: _____ Date: _____

Linking Literacy
During-Reading

Cause and Effect

Directions: Write the effect for each cause below. There can be more than one effect for each cause. Then draw a picture to illustrate each one.

Cause	Effect	Illustration
Rotation →		
Earth's Axis →		
Revolution →		

Linking Literacy
Post-Reading

Act It Out

After reading the text, plan a way to act out rotation and revolution. Use the space below to plan your act. Draw how you will move and label what each person will represent. One person from the group should narrate and describe what is being acted out. Be sure to include the Sun and Earth, Earth's tilt, and the day-and-night cycle.

Narration

_____

_____

_____

_____

_____

_____

Reading Science

Earth Interacts

1. It may seem like Earth is always changing—and it is! But many of these changes form patterns, which means the changes repeat over and over again. In fact, there are patterns all around us.

2. Take the tides, for example. If you build a sand castle and leave it on the beach, it will most likely be gone by the morning. Why? This happens because of high and low tides. High tide means that the water comes up higher on the land. Low tide means that the water flows back out. High tide and low tide each happen twice in a 24-hour day. So, when the tide is high, water will cover up the parts of the beach where you may have built a sand castle during the low tide.

3. High and low tides are caused by the position of the Moon. Sure, the Moon is over 200,000 miles away, but it is so large that its gravity affects the water on Earth. The pull of the Moon's gravity is strongest when the Moon is more directly facing our part of Earth. That is when high tide occurs. When the Moon is not facing our part of Earth, its pull is not as strong. That is when low tides occur.

4. You can observe another pattern by looking at the Moon itself. The way the Moon looks changes from night to night. Sometimes, you see a full Moon, and sometimes, you see a half Moon. Sometimes, the Moon is not visible at all. It all depends on the positions of the Sun, Earth, and the Moon. But, the phases of the Moon (shapes of the Moon that we see from Earth) are always predictable. They happen in the same order, over and over again.

5. We see these phases because only one-half of the Moon's surface is facing the Sun at any given time. At different times of the month, we can see different parts of the Moon's lit surface because of where we are **positioned** in the Earth-Sun-Moon system.

6. The seasons are another pattern caused by the positions of Earth and the Sun. Earth is tilted and travels in an orbit around the Sun. Our summer occurs when Earth's Northern Hemisphere is tilted toward the Sun as it moves along its orbit. During this time, the Northern Hemisphere receives stronger, more-concentrated rays from the Sun, which causes the warmer temperatures during summer. In winter, temperatures are colder, because the Northern Hemisphere points away from the Sun and receives less-direct heat from the Sun. This means that during our winter, the Southern Hemisphere is tilted toward the Sun, so they are having their summer!

7. Yes, Earth may always be changing. But we can predict many of these changes because they happen in the same way over and over again.

Reading Science

1. What is the best summary of this passage?

    A.   The Moon phases are caused by the positions of the Sun, Earth, and the Moon.

    B.   Tides are caused by the position of the Moon.

    C.   Seasons are caused by the positions of the Sun and Earth.

    D.   Many patterns are caused by the positions of objects in the solar system.

2. If you build a sand castle and it disappears, it is probably because–

    A.   kids knocked it over in the night.

    B.   low tide made the water level go down.

    C.   high tide raised the water level.

    D.   the positions of Earth, the Sun, and the Moon caused a change in the Moon phases.

3. What is the best synonym for the word **position** (fifth paragraph)?

    A.   Placement

    B.   Orbit

    C.   Phase

    D.   Shadow

Reading Science

4. What is something that might happen at low tide?

    A.   Things on the beach will be washed away.

    B.   People who are not careful might be trapped by rising water.

    C.   The Moon's gravity will cause the water to rise.

    D.   You can walk on the beach in places that were underwater earlier in the day.

5. What is an example of another pattern in nature that is caused by the positions of objects in the solar system?

    A.   The petals of a flower

    B.   Zebra stripes

    C.   Day and night

    D.   A bee's honeycomb

Name: _____ Date: _____

 **Open-Ended Response**

1. When you walk outside in the morning, you notice a shadow on the ground from a tree in your yard. When you get home in the afternoon, you notice the shadow is in a different place. Why did the shadow move?

_____

_____

_____

_____

_____

_____

2. Does everyone on Earth experience night at the same time? Why or why not?

_____

_____

_____

_____

_____

_____

3. If Earth rotated at a greater speed on its axis, what would happen to the length of each day on Earth?

_____

_____

_____

_____

_____

_____

Claim-Evidence-Reasoning

Scenario

Mrs. Rollin's class noticed that the flagpole outside casts a shadow on the ground each day, and the shadow seems to always be moving and changing lengths. The students decided to observe and measure the flagpole's shadow for several days. Below is the data the class collected.

Shadow Direction					
	8:00 a.m.	10:00 a.m.	12:00 p.m. (noon)	2:00 p.m.	4:00 p.m.
Day 1	W	NW	N	NE	E
Day 2	W	NW	N	NE	E
Day 3	W	NW	N	NE	E
Day 4	W	NW	N	NE	E

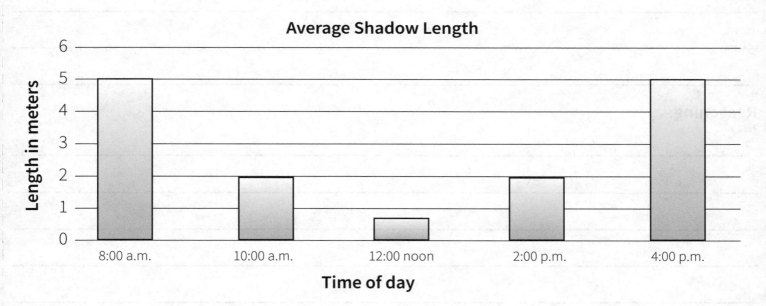

The students also observed the Sun was in the eastern sky at 8:00 a.m. and appeared to rise until it was overhead at noon. The Sun then appeared to go down in the western sky. At 4:00 p.m., the Sun was in the western sky.

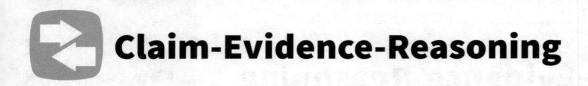

Claim-Evidence-Reasoning

Prompt

Use the data table and graph to write a scientific explanation describing what the class could expect to observe on Day 5 at 2:00 p.m.

Claim:

_____

_____

_____

_____

Evidence:

_____

_____

_____

_____

_____

Reasoning:

_____

_____

_____

_____

_____

_____

Observing the Stars

Graphic Organizer

The Sun and Other Stars

Directions: Our Sun is a star. Think about what makes our Sun unique and what makes it the same as other stars. Use the Venn diagram to compare and contrast the Sun with other stars.

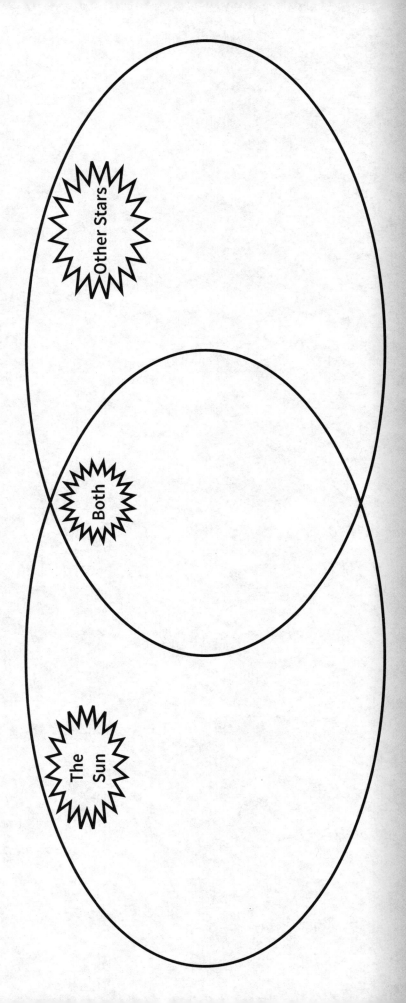

The Sun

Both

Other Stars

Explore 1

Star Model

Draw a blueprint for your model. Include labels and the scale you will use to build it.

What are some reasons why your model may not be completely correct?

_____

_____

_____

Do you think each star looks the same from Earth? Explain your answer.

_____

_____

_____

 **Explore 1**

Star Model

Claim-Evidence-Reasoning

Prompt

Use the information from the activity to complete the following task.

Compare the following pictures with your model. Write a scientific explanation about why some stars appear brighter and larger than others.

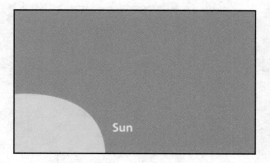

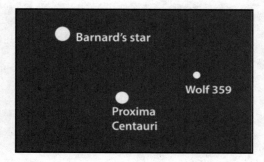

Claim:

_____

_____

Evidence:

_____

_____

Reasoning:

_____

_____

_____

_____

Linking Literacy
Pre-Reading

3-2-1 Notes

Before you read: Complete the table below.

# 3 **3** Things You Know about Stars	• _____ _____ • _____ _____ • _____ _____
# 2 **2** Examples of How We Know Stars Are near Earth	• _____ _____ • _____ _____
# 1 **1** Question You Have about Stars	• _____ _____ _____

Linking Literacy
During-Reading

Observing the Stars: CLOZE-ing In

While reading, fill in the blanks with words from the text.

Stars are classified by their size, color, brightness, mass, and surface temperature.

Size

A star's size is measured as a ratio of the size of the _____ . The Sun's diameter is called 1 solar _____ , so a star with a measurement of 0.75 solar diameter is equal in size to three-fourths of the Sun.

Distance

The _____ of stars can appear larger if they are closer to Earth than other stars. Although the Sun appears much _____ than the stars we see at night, it is not the largest star.

Light-Years

Because stars are so far apart, we have a special unit of_____ we use to measure them. The distance of a star from Earth is measured in light-years. A light-year is equal to the distance that _____ travels (through space) in _____ year. A light-year is equal to about 5,878,499,810,000 miles, or 9,500,000,000,000 km.

Star	Distance in Light-Years
Sirius	_____
Alpha Centauri	4.3
Betelgeuse	1,400
Achernar	_____

Observing the Stars

Linking Literacy
Post-Reading

Observing the Stars Table

Directions: Use the table provided to draw and describe each star's characteristics in reference to each other, including size and distance.

	Color	Solar Radius in Miles	Distance in Light-Years
Sirius A	White	740,000	8.6
Alpha Centauri A	Yellow	528,500	4.3
Betelgeuse	Red	600 million	1,400
Achernar	Blue	5.2 million	69

Sirius	**Alpha Centauri**

Betelgeuse	Achernar
_____	_____
_____	_____
_____	_____
_____	_____
_____	_____
_____	_____
_____	_____

Reading Science

The Stars at Night

1. "Are we finally here, Dad?" asked five-year-old Jimmy as he impatiently kicked the back of the car seat. Jimmy and his dad had left their house for a camping trip, and Jimmy was anxious to be out of the car. Jimmy's dad peered out of the window and, after spotting their campsite, he pulled into their parking spot and put the car into park.

2. "We're here!" his dad declared. Jimmy climbed out of the car and gazed up at the night sky full of twinkling stars. "How about we grab some blankets and look at the stars before we get unpacked?"

3. Jimmy definitely did not want to unpack, so he agreed and quickly brought out some blankets from the car. As his dad spread the blankets, Jimmy stared up at the stars in astonishment. Back home, there was never a single star in the sky, but here, Jimmy saw so many. They looked like millions of holiday lights flickering; they decorated the night sky.

4. Jimmy and his dad laid on the blankets and stared up at the night sky. He saw all the different shapes the stars made up. He could see an outline of a tree, an apple, and a pyramid. Jimmy pointed them out to his dad, and soon he, too, had found outlines of his own. Jimmy's dad explained that groups of stars that form a pattern are called *constellations*.

5. "Look, Jimmy! That group of stars over there looks like a tent! Speaking of that, we should probably get ours set up; it's getting late," Jimmy's dad said. Jimmy sighed and started to unpack. No more time to look at stars. His dad patted him on the back. "Don't worry, Son. They'll be here tomorrow. We can look for more shapes then," he said. Jimmy smiled and started to get his camping gear out of the car. Soon, the tent was up, and Jimmy laid out his sleeping bag.

6. "I'm tired. Can we go to sleep?" Jimmy yawned as he climbed into his sleeping bag. His dad nodded and turned off the lantern. Jimmy quickly fell asleep to the sound of crickets chirping and images of stars in his head.

Reading Science

7. Sunshine washed into the tent the next morning and woke Jimmy up. He rubbed his eyes and saw that his dad was already up and making breakfast.

8. "Good morning, Jimmy! Did the bright Sun wake you?" Jimmy nodded as he looked up at the sky. All he could see was the bright, yellow Sun and the clear, blue sky.

9. "Wait, where are all the stars? I thought you said there would be more today," Jimmy questioned, shielding his eyes from the radiant Sun. He walked over to his dad and started eating a piece of bacon that his dad had finished preparing.

10. "Oh, we have to wait until the nighttime to see those stars, Jimmy," his dad answered. *So, there are no stars at all during the day*? Jimmy wondered. As if he was reading his thoughts, his dad continued. "But there is one star that you are guaranteed to see every day; the Sun. The Sun is, in fact, a medium-sized star."

11. Jimmy glanced at the Sun, but quickly turned away from the brightness. "But why is it so bright? I was able to look at the stars last night, but the Sun burns my eyes!"

12. Jimmy's dad laughed. "The Sun is so bright because it is closer; that's why we can't even look at it," his dad informed him. His dad went on to explain, "The stars last night are millions, maybe even a billion, miles away from us. Since they are so far away from us, the stars are not that bright to our eye. The Sun is much closer to us; therefore, we can see it better. It is around 90 million miles away from us, which I know seems far, but for a star, that is actually close. During the day, the Sun makes our sky so bright that we cannot see the much-dimmer stars. At night, when the sky is dark, we can see the light of the other stars." Jimmy finished his piece of bacon.

13. "So, on our hike today, can I use your hat? I don't want my eyes to burn!" Jimmy said. His dad chuckled and put his hat on Jimmy's head.

14. "Sure! And don't worry, we'll be able to look at all the other stars tonight," his dad replied as he gave Jimmy a piece of toast. Jimmy smiled; he was not worried. Now he knew once the sky was dark enough, he would be able to see all those stars again. He could not wait!

Reading Science

1. What will probably happen at the end of Jimmy and his father's day?

   A.   They will go home, since they have a long drive ahead of them.

   B.   Jimmy will be tired from his hike and go to bed early.

   C.   Jimmy and his father will stargaze and find more star shapes.

   D.   Jimmy's father will finish unpacking and setting up camp.

2. Read this sentence from the selection:

   They looked like millions of holiday lights flickering; they decorated the night sky.

   The imagery used in this line appeals most to the reader's sense of–

   A.   sight.

   B.   smell.

   C.   taste.

   D.   hearing.

3. Which sentence best supports the idea that the Sun is Earth's closest star?

   A.   *"The Sun is, in fact, a medium-sized star."*

   B.   *"The Sun is much closer to us; therefore, we can see it better."*

   C.   *Jimmy glanced at the Sun, but quickly turned away from the brightness.*

   D.   *"The stars last night are millions, maybe even a billion, miles away from us."*

4. Which is the best summary for this story?

A. Jimmy and his father were on a camping trip. Jimmy noticed all the stars in the night sky. He found groups of stars that made shapes. The next day, Jimmy was disappointed that the stars were gone. Jimmy's dad explained that there was a star that was visible—the Sun. Jimmy learned why people see the Sun during the day. He was excited for nighttime so that he and his dad could see the night stars again.

B. Jimmy and his father drove hours to reach their campsite. Once there, they decided to look at the stars before they unpacked and set up camp. Jimmy could not believe how many stars were in the night sky. Jimmy and his father found groups of stars that made shapes. Finally, Jimmy grew tired, and Jimmy and his father went to sleep in their tent.

C. Jimmy and his father were camping. The first night Jimmy and his father stargazed before setting up their camp. The next morning, Jimmy and his father ate breakfast and then got ready to go on a hike. Jimmy wanted to wear his father's hat, because the Sun was so bright. Jimmy was looking forward to nighttime, so he could look at the stars again.

D. Jimmy and his father were camping. Jimmy did not understand why he saw so many stars at night, but not during the day. Jimmy's father explained that the stars seen at night were billions of miles from Earth, but our Sun was a star that was visible during the day, because it was our closest star. Jimmy tried to look at the Sun, but he realized it was too bright. He asked to wear his dad's hat to help keep the Sun out of his eyes.

5. All these statements support the idea that Jimmy was confused about stars, except–

A. *So, there are no stars at all during the day? Jimmy wondered.*

B. *"But why is it so bright? I was able to look at the stars last night, but the Sun burns my eyes!"*

C. *"Wait, where are all the stars? I thought you said there would be more today," Jimmy questioned.*

D. *Now he knew once the sky was dark enough, he would be able to see all those stars again.*

Name: _____ Date: _____

Open-Ended Response

Short Answer

1. Describe the forms of energy that the Sun provides to Earth.

_____

_____

_____

_____

_____

_____

2. We know our Sun is a star. Why do we see other stars as only tiny specks in the sky?

_____

_____

_____

_____

_____

_____

3. What characteristic affects how bright a star appears to us?

_____

_____

_____

_____

_____

Claim-Evidence-Reasoning

Scenario

The two planets that appear below are orbiting around the same star (our Sun). Use the picture examples to help determine the apparent proximity of the Sun to each of the planets.

A

B

Prompt

Write a scientific explanation describing which planet is closest to the Sun.

Claim:

_____

_____

_____

_____

_____

Claim-Evidence-Reasoning

Evidence:

_____

_____

_____

_____

_____

Reasoning:

_____

_____

_____

_____

_____

_____

_____

Objects In The Sky

Graphic Organizer

The Sun, the Moon, and Stars

Directions: Fill in the cause-and-effect charts below.

Cause		Effect
	Pattern repeats every _____	The Moon appears to change shape
Cause		Effect
	Pattern repeats every _____	Constellations only visible sometimes
Cause		Effect
	Pattern repeats every _____	Length of daylight changes over time

Explore 1

Moon Phase Experience

What patterns of light did you notice as you were modeling the phases of the Moon? Draw a picture of the pattern you observed.

1. Describe the pattern you observed.

_____

2. How could this pattern be helpful in the future?

_____

_____

3. What data or observations could you use as evidence to prove that objects in the sky look different at different times?

_____

_____

_____

Name: _____ Date: _____

Explore 2

Up in the Wonderful Sky

Draw a diagram showing the movement of Earth, the Sun, and the stars. Be sure to add labels.

Do the stars (constellations) stay in one spot, or do they move? Explain your answer.

_____

_____

_____

_____

Why are certain constellations visible only during specific times of the year?

_____

_____

_____

_____

 **Explore 2**

Up in the Wonderful Sky
Claim - Evidence - Reasoning

Prompt

Using scientific reasoning, describe whether all constellations can be seen throughout the year.

Claim:

_____

_____

_____

Evidence:

_____

_____

_____

Reasoning:

_____

_____

_____

_____

Explore 3

Sunrise, Sunset!

Part I

1. Draw and label your rotation model.

2. As you rotate your model at each position, record your data in the tables below.

Month	First City to Enter Lighted Area	Last City to Leave Lighted Area
December		
March		
June		
September		

Month	Width of Lighted Area: City A	Width of Lighted Area: City B
December		
March		
June		
September		

Explore 3

3. What did you notice about December and June?

_____

_____

4. What did you notice about March and September?

_____

_____

5. How does the length of day and night change during the year for City A?

_____

_____

6. Why do we receive more daylight during certain times of the year?

_____

_____

7. Draw the positions of Earth and the Sun during June and December. Be sure to include Earth's axis to show its tilt.

June	December

Explore 3

Part II

On the chart below, record the time of sunrise and sunset as well as the length of day for your hometown (City A) and for a city in the Southern Hemisphere. You can choose one of these cities for City B: Santiago, Chile; Rio de Janeiro, Brazil; or Buenos Aires, Argentina.

	City A		City B	
	Sunrise	Sunset	Sunrise	Sunset
Winter December 21				
	Length of Day		Length of Day	
	Sunrise	Sunset	Sunrise	Sunset
Spring March 21				
	Length of Day		Length of Day	
	Sunrise	Sunset	Sunrise	Sunset
Summer June 21				
	Length of Day		Length of Day	
	Sunrise	Sunset	Sunrise	Sunset
Fall September 21				
	Length of Day		Length of Day	

1. How do you determine the length of a day?

2. Use the data you recorded on the chart to create a graph showing the length of day during the different seasons. Include labels on each axis as well as a key.

Key

Sunrise, Sunset!

Explore 3

Use the data from the chart and graph to answer the following questions.

1. When are the days the longest?

_____

_____

_____

2. When are the days the shortest?

_____

_____

_____

3. Describe the length of day in the spring and fall.

_____

_____

_____

4. What pattern do you notice in the length of day in the different seasons?

_____

_____

_____

5. Knowing this pattern, what can you predict about the length of days next winter?

_____

_____

_____

Explore 3

Sunrise, Sunset!

Claim-Evidence-Reasoning

Prompt

Think about the length of the days in the different seasons. Compare the length of the days in the winter to the length of days in the spring, summer, and fall for City A.

Claim:

_____

_____

_____

_____

Evidence:

_____

_____

_____

_____

Reasoning:

_____

_____

_____

_____

_____

Linking Literacy
During-Reading

Main Ideas and Details

While you read: Look for details in the text that give more information about the six main ideas listed below. Write two details for every main idea.

Text Topic: **What is the Sun?**

Page	Main Idea:	Detail 1:	Detail 2:

Text Topic: **What is the Moon?**

Page	Main Idea:	Detail 1:	Detail 2:

Text Topic: **What causes the changing appearance of the Moon?**

Page	Main Idea:	Detail 1:	Detail 2:

Linking Literacy
During-Reading

Text Topic: What is a planetarium?

Page	Main Idea:	Detail 1:	Detail 2:

Text Topic: Constellations

Page	Main Idea:	Detail 1:	Detail 2:

Text Topic: Patterns

Page	Main Idea:	Detail 1:	Detail 2:

Linking Literacy
Post-Reading

Web Chirps

Summarize what you have learned about each topic from the reading into a web chirp. Make sure you use fewer than 140 characters in each summary.

The Sun

_____

@_____

_____

_____

_____

_____

The Moon

_____

@_____

_____

_____

_____

_____

Linking Literacy
Post-Reading

Constellations

_____
@_____

_____

_____

_____

_____

Patterns

_____
@_____

_____

_____

_____

_____

Reading Science

The Sky and Our Calendar

1. For thousands of years, people have used the Sun, the Moon, and stars to keep track of time. While looking at the sky, they have noticed how certain patterns repeat, and they have used those patterns to make calendars. Most of the time, these patterns make it easy for us to keep track of time. But not always!

2. For example, deciding on the length of a year can be harder than you might think. A day is exactly 24 hours. That is how long it takes Earth to rotate once. And we say that a year is 365 days because that is the time it takes Earth to travel once around the Sun. But, that is not quite true! Earth's trip around the Sun actually takes 365 days—plus a fraction of another day. This fraction of a day complicates our calendar. We solved the problem by adding an extra day to the calendar every fourth year. Most years, February has 28 days. But during a leap year, February has an additional day, the 29th. This way, we can keep our calendar on track.

3. Figuring out the length of a month has also caused problems. For example, many cultures in history have used a **lunar** calendar. A lunar calendar is based on the cycle of the Moon, which takes about a month. This means that there are about 12½ lunar months in a year. But, different cultures have chosen to start their months at different parts of the Moon's cycle. The Hebrew and Islamic calendars, for example, start a new month when a thin crescent Moon is barely visible. But the Chinese calendar, on the other hand, starts a new month the moment the new Moon rises. This made it hard for these cultures to communicate and trade.

4. In the 1500s, England had problems with their calendar. The English divided the month into weeks, just as we do today. They decided that every month should have 4 weeks. This meant that 1 week was actually a little longer than 7 days. Also, it meant that there were 13 months to a year. By the 20th century, however, most countries had adopted the same calendar. This made trade and communication between them easier. Some countries still had to drop 13 days from their calendar, because their old way of counting months and years did not line up with the new ways of counting.

5. The Sun, the Moon, Earth, and stars move in predictable cycles. But even though these patterns occur regularly, we have never figured out a simple way to make a calendar that works just right.

Reading Science

1. How long does it take Earth to travel around the Sun?

    A. 1 month

    B. 1 day

    C. 1 year

    D. 1 lunar month

2. Which is the process described by the two phrases below?

> 1. Takes approximately 24 hours
> 2. Is the result of the rotation of Earth

    A. 1 year

    B. 1 month

    C. 1 day

    D. 1 revolution of the Moon

3. The word **lunar** (paragraph 3) means–

    A. having to do with calendars.

    B. having to do with the Moon.

    C. yearly.

    D. crazy.

 **Reading Science**

4. What is a problem that would likely occur if two cultures had different calendars?

    A. They might have different languages.

    B. They might have a war about which calendar is better.

    C. They might misunderstand dates when they try to communicate.

    D. They might not know how long it takes the Moon's phases to cycle.

5. The author organizes this passage by–

    A. telling the reader the effects caused by Earth's rotation.

    B. sequencing the changes in calendars that have occurred through the years.

    C. explaining the problems people have had with making calendars.

    D. telling a story about calendars.

Open-Ended Response

1. We can easily see the constellation Leo from the months of March to May. Why are constellations not seen in the same place in the sky all year round?

_____

_____

_____

_____

_____

2. Why are summer days longer than winter days?

_____

_____

_____

_____

_____

3. Your teacher asks you to create models of Earth, the Sun, and the Moon. What materials would you use to represent each object? Why?

_____

_____

_____

_____

_____

_____

Name: _____ Date: _____

Claim-Evidence-Reasoning

Scenario

One October night, Shea was visiting Mary at her home. Mary told Shea that when her grandfather had visited in April he had taught her how to identify the constellations Leo, Orion, and Ursa Major. The girls went outside to find the constellations. They found Ursa Major but could not find Leo or Orion. Shea thinks the night sky always looks the same and that Mary must have made a mistake. The images below show what the night sky looked like in October and in April.

Night Sky in October

NORTH

Ursa Major
Auriga
Ursa Minor
Cassiopeia
Corona Borealis
Cepheus
Lyra
Hercules
Perseus
Cygnus
EAST
WEST
Aries
Taurus
Pegasus
Aquila
Pisces
Sagittarius
Aquarius
Capricornus

SOUTH

Night Sky in April

NORTH

Cepheus
Cassiopeia
Hercules
Perseus
Ursa Minor
Auriga
Corona Borealis
Taurus
EAST
Bootes
Ursa Major
Gemini
WEST
Cancer
Orion
Canis Minor
Leo
Libra
Virgo
Canis Major

SOUTH

Prompt

Write a scientific explanation describing if the night sky looks the same all year. Be sure to support your claim with evidence and reasoning.

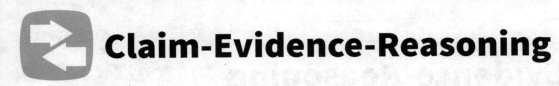

Claim-Evidence-Reasoning

Claim:

_____

_____

_____

_____

Evidence:

_____

_____

_____

_____

_____

_____

Reasoning:

_____

_____

_____

_____

_____

_____

_____